Scott Foresman

Grade 6
Unit and End-of-Year
Benchmark Tests
Teacher's Manual

PEARSON

Glenview, Illinois • Boston, Massachusetts • Chandler, Arizona • Upper Saddle River, New Jersey

The Pearson Promise

As the largest educational publishing company in the world, Pearson is committed to providing you with curriculum that not only meets the Common Core State Standards, but also supports your implementation of these standards with your students.

Pearson has aligned the Common Core State Standards to every grade level of *Scott Foresman Reading Street,* our premier educational curriculum. This product provides an alignment of the Common Core State Standards to the Grade 6 assessment items in *Scott Foresman Reading Street Unit and End-of-Year Benchmark Tests.*

We value your partnership highly and look forward to continuing our mission to provide educational materials that fully satisfy your classroom needs.

ISBN-13: 978-0-328-68396-3
ISBN-10: 0-328-68396-5
7 8 9 10 V001 15 14 13

Contents

OVERVIEW

Scott Foresman *Reading Street* provides a wide array of formal tests and classroom assessments to support instruction. Formal assessments include the following:

- Baseline Group Tests

- Weekly Selection Tests

- Fresh Reads for Differentiated Test Practice

- Unit and End-of-Year Benchmark Tests aligned to Common Core State Standards

This Teacher's Manual includes the Benchmark Tests and provides information for administering them, scoring them, and interpreting their results. Detailed information about other assessment materials and procedures may be found in the *Assessment Handbook*.

Description of the Benchmark Tests

In Grade 6, there are six Unit Benchmark Tests—one for each unit—and an End-of-Year Benchmark Test. The Unit Benchmark Tests are designed to measure student progress based on the comprehension skills and strategies, literary genres, themes, vocabulary, writing conventions, and types of writing taught in each unit. The End-of-Year Benchmark Test measures skills covered in all six units. The Benchmark Tests offer an integrated approach to assessment by measuring all skills and strategies in relation to reading selections.

In addition, the Benchmark Tests are designed to provide practice in test-taking skills and to prepare students to take the Reading/Language Arts section of standardized tests, state tests, or teacher-made tests. The tests include both multiple-choice and constructed-response questions. They also include writing prompts that will help students prepare for state writing tests.

Each Unit Benchmark Test has these features:

- Each test has two components—Reading – Parts 1–3 and Writing – Part 4.

- Reading – Part 1 presents two selections in different genres. The genres of these selections, drawn from fiction and nonfiction, reflect genres taught in each unit.

- Each selection reflects the theme of the unit.

- Reading – Parts 1–3 contain forty multiple-choice questions and two constructed-response questions. These questions test reading comprehension, literary skills and genre, critical-thinking skills, vocabulary strategies, and writing conventions. Some of the items measure the ability to synthesize information and to compare and contrast across texts.

- Writing – Part 4 of each test presents a writing prompt based on one of the types of writing taught in the unit. These prompts are similar to those found in state writing tests.

The End-of-Year Benchmark Test follows the same design as the Unit Benchmark Tests, but it has more selections and items. It measures selected skills from all six units taught during the year.

The Benchmark Tests are designed to assess student progress at the end of each unit and at the end of the school year. Selections and questions in the Unit Benchmark Tests become progressively more difficult from Unit 1 to Unit 6 to reflect the increasing sophistication of materials students are able to handle.

ADMINISTERING THE TESTS

The Benchmark Tests are designed for group administration. You may decide to administer each test in one sitting, or you may administer parts of the test in two or more sittings. (If you administer the test in two or more sittings, try to schedule the sittings on the same day or within a day of the previous sitting because some of the questions at the end of the test compare and contrast selections.)

These tests were designed to give teachers the option of separating multiple-choice questions from the constructed-response questions. You may opt to have students skip the constructed-response questions in order to create an all multiple-choice test.

These tests are not intended to be timed. We recommend allowing ample time for all students to complete the tests at their own pace. However, for the purposes of scheduling, planning, and practicing timed-test situations, the chart below shows the number of items in each test part and the estimated amount of time required to complete each part.

Test Part	Number of Items	Estimated Time
Reading – Part 1 (Selection 1)	11 multiple-choice	20–25 minutes
	1 constructed-response	5 minutes
Reading – Part 1 (Selection 2)	11 multiple-choice	20–25 minutes
	1 constructed-response	5 minutes
Reading – Part 2 (Vocabulary)	10 multiple-choice	20 minutes
Reading – Part 3 (Writing Conventions)	8 multiple-choice	15–20 minutes
Writing – Part 4 (OPTIONAL)	1 writing prompt	45 minutes

The End-of-Year Benchmark Test has longer selections, sixty multiple-choice items, two constructed-response items, and one writing prompt. To administer the End-of-Year Test, plan on about two hours for Reading – Parts 1–3 and forty-five minutes for Writing – Part 4.

Benchmark Test Teacher's Manual

Directions for Administering the Tests

Before you administer a test . . .

Review the test directions below and on pages T8–T9. Modify the directions as needed based on how you decide to administer each test. For Reading – Parts 1–3, students can mark their responses directly on their tests or on the Bubble Answer Sheets included for copy on pages T57–T58. In Writing – Part 4 of all tests, students write compositions in response to a prompt. They write their compositions on the lined pages in their test booklets. You may wish to provide scrap paper that students can use to plan their writing. Only the writing in their test booklets will be scored.

When you are ready to administer a test . . .

Distribute a test to each student. Have students write their names on the front of their test booklets, their answer sheets, and on any additional sheets of paper they may use. Have students flip through the test as you point out and explain its key features. For example, point out directions, selection titles, selections, art, Go On and Stop symbols, multiple-choice questions with answer choices, constructed-response questions with lines for written responses, and the writing prompt with a checklist and two lined pages for the compositions. Allow time for students to ask any questions they may have about the test's contents before you begin the test.

Directions in **bold** type that follow are intended to be read aloud. Other directions are intended for your information only. For Reading – Part 1, modify the general directions as needed if you intend to skip the constructed-response questions. For Writing – Part 4, you may wish to modify directions about the amount of time suggested for the testing session to match the time allowed for your state's writing tests.

Directions for Reading – Part 1: Comprehension

In the first part of this test, you will read two selections and answer some questions about them. There are two types of questions: multiple-choice questions and questions that require you to write short answers.

If you are having students mark their answers to the multiple-choice questions directly on their tests, then say:

Mark your answers to the multiple-choice questions in your test. For each question, circle the letter that goes with the answer you choose. If you want to change your answer, completely erase the circle you made and circle a different letter. Do not make any other marks in your test.

If students are marking their answers to the multiple-choice questions on answer sheets, then say:

Mark your answers to the multiple-choice questions on your answer sheet. For each question, fill in the circle on your answer sheet that goes with the answer you choose. Fill in the circle completely and make your mark heavy and dark. If you want to change your answer, completely erase the mark you made and fill in a different circle. Do not make any other marks on your answer sheet.

For all students, say:

For Questions A and B, write your answers on the lines in your test. Think carefully and write your ideas as clearly as you can. Allow about five minutes to answer each of these questions.

Read the directions carefully. You can ask me to explain any directions you do not understand. Read the selections and the questions very carefully. You may look back at a selection as often as you like to help you answer the questions.

Answer the questions you are sure about first. If a question seems too difficult, skip it and go back to it later. Check each answer to make sure it is the best answer for the question asked.

Think positively. Some questions may seem hard, but others will be easy. Relax. Most people get nervous about tests. It's natural. Just do your best.

Continue with Reading – Part 1: Comprehension until you come to a STOP sign at the end of Question B. When you have completed that question, put your pencils down, close your test booklets, and look up.

Tell students how much of the test they are expected to complete in this sitting and how much time they have to complete their work. Allow time for students to ask questions about the directions. Then direct students to open their tests to a specified page and begin. You may wish to give students a break upon completion of this part of the test.

Directions for Reading – Part 2 and Optional Part 3

Read aloud the directions from the student book for Parts 2 and 3. Tell students how much time they have to complete their work for each part of the test. Point out the STOP sign at the end of each part, instructing them to put their pencils down and look up whenever they come to a STOP sign. That way you can wait for all students to complete the section before moving on to the next part.

Directions for Writing – Part 4 (Optional)

For the last part of the test, you will do a writing exercise. The writing prompt in your test explains what you are going to write about and gives you some ideas for planning your writing. Before you begin writing, think about what you want to say and how you want to say it. You can use scrap paper to jot down your ideas.

After planning what you will write, write your composition on the two lined pages in your test. Be sure that your writing does what the prompt asks you to do. Only the writing in your test booklet will be scored.

Your writing may be about something that is real or make-believe, but remember, you are to write ONLY about the prompt in your test.

You may give your writing a title if you would like. However, a title is not required.

You may NOT use a dictionary. If you do not know how to spell a word, sound out the word and do the best you can.

You may either print or write in cursive. It is important to write as neatly as possible.

Your writing should be easy to read and should show that you can organize and express your thoughts clearly and completely.

I cannot read the prompt to you or help you plan what to write. You must read and plan yourself. Remember to read the prompt first and then plan what you will write.

You have a total of forty-five minutes to read, plan, and respond to your prompt. I will let you know when you have ten minutes left. (You may wish to modify the amount of time you allow for Writing – Part 4 to match the time allowed on your state's writing tests.)

If you finish early, please proofread your composition. Revise and edit the writing in your test. Use the questions in the Checklist for Writers to help you check your composition.

Allow time for students to ask any questions about the directions. Then direct students to open their tests to the writing prompt page, read the prompt, plan their writing, and then write their compositions. Be sure to alert students when they have 10 minutes left.

After testing . . .

Once students are finished testing, collect all test booklets and answer sheets. Directions for scoring the tests begin on page T10. The answer keys begin on page T47. Evaluation charts with alignments to Common Core State Standards (T31–T44) are provided along with a class record chart on page T45.

SCORING THE TESTS

The Benchmark Tests are intended to be scored by part—a total score for Reading – Parts 1–3 and a separate score for Writing – Part 4. To make scoring easier, copy and use the following charts as needed:

- the Unit Benchmark Test Evaluation Charts, beginning on page T31, for recording a student's individual scores on a Unit Benchmark Test;

- the End-of-Year Benchmark Test Evaluation Chart, on pages T43 and T44, for recording a student's individual scores on the End-of-Year Benchmark Test; and

- the Class Record Chart, on page T45, for recording test scores for all students for all six units.

Answer keys for each test begin on page T47. In Reading – Part 1, there are two types of items: multiple-choice questions and constructed-response questions. These types of items are scored in slightly different ways, as explained below. In Writing – Part 4, each prompt is linked to one of four different types of writing: narrative, descriptive, expository, or persuasive. For each type of writing, there are four Writing Scoring Rubrics. Each rubric has a different point scale. Choose the rubric that most closely matches the rubric for your state's writing tests or the rubric you deem most appropriate for your students. Writing Scoring Rubrics begin on page T12.

Scoring Multiple-Choice Questions

Each multiple-choice question has four answer choices labeled A, B, C, D or F, G, H, J. Refer to the answer key for the test you are scoring and mark each multiple-choice question as either correct (1 point) or incorrect (0 points).

Scoring Constructed-Response Questions

Use the answer keys and the rubric on page T11 to help you score constructed-response questions. Award each constructed-response answer a score from 0 to 2 points, depending on how accurate and complete the response is. The answer keys provide abbreviated descriptions of top responses. Have an ideal top response in mind before you assess students' responses.

Constructed-Response Scoring Rubric

Points	Description
2	The response indicates a **full understanding** of the question's reading or critical-thinking skill. The response is accurate and complete. Necessary support and/or examples are included, and the information is clearly text-based.
1	The response indicates a **partial understanding** of the question's reading or critical-thinking skill. The response includes information that is essentially correct and text-based, but it is too general or too simplistic. Some of the support and/or examples may be incomplete or omitted.
0	The response is **inaccurate,** confused, and/or irrelevant, or the student has failed to respond to the task.

Scoring Writing – Part 4

To evaluate students' responses to a writing prompt, familiarize yourself with the writing prompt and review the Writing Scoring Rubrics on pages T12–T19. Identify the type of writing suggested in the writing prompt. (Types of writing for each prompt are identified in the answer keys that begin on page T47.) Then choose one of the four Writing Scoring Rubrics provided for that type of writing. Use the rubric to score each composition on a scale from 1 to 6, 1 to 5, 1 to 4, or 1 to 3.

Writing Scoring Rubrics: Narrative Writing

6-Point Scoring Rubric

6	5	4	3	2	1
narrative writing is well focused on the topic	narrative writing is focused on the topic	narrative writing is generally focused on the topic	narrative writing is generally focused but may stray from the topic	narrative writing is minimally related to the topic	narrative writing is not focused on the topic
contains clear ideas	most ideas are clear	ideas are generally clear	ideas may be somewhat unclear	ideas are often unclear	ideas are unclear
logically organized; uses transitions	logically organized; uses some transitions	logically organized with some lapses; has transitions	somewhat organized; may lack transitions	minimally organized; no transitions	unorganized; no transitions
voice is engaging; well suited to purpose and audience	voice comes through well; suited to purpose and audience	voice comes through occasionally; suited to purpose and audience	voice uneven; not always suited to purpose or audience	slight evidence of voice; little sense of purpose or audience	weak voice; no sense of purpose or audience
demonstrates varied, precise word choice	generally demonstrates varied, precise word choice	often demonstrates varied, precise word choice	word choice could be more varied, precise	poor choice of words; limited vocabulary	limited vocabulary
sentences are complete, fluent, and varied	most sentences are complete and varied	many sentences are complete and varied	some incomplete sentences; little variety	sentences are incomplete; show little or no variety	gross errors in sentence structure; no variety
shows excellent control of writing conventions	shows very good control of writing conventions	shows good control of writing conventions	shows fair control of writing conventions	shows frequent errors in writing conventions	shows many serious errors in writing conventions

5-Point Scoring Rubric

5	4	3	2	1
narrative writing is well focused on the topic	narrative writing is focused on the topic	narrative writing is generally focused on the topic	narrative writing strays from the topic	narrative writing is not focused on the topic
contains clear ideas	most ideas are clear	ideas are generally clear	many ideas are unclear	ideas are unclear
logically organized; uses transitions	logically organized; uses some transitions	logically organized with some lapses; transitions weak	little organization; few or no transitions	unorganized; no transitions
voice is engaging; well suited to purpose and audience	voice is fairly strong; suited to purpose and audience	voice comes through occasionally; may not suit purpose or audience	voice comes through rarely; poorly suited to purpose or audience	weak voice; no sense of audience or purpose
demonstrates varied, precise word choice	generally demonstrates varied, precise word choice	word choice could be more varied, precise	poor choice of words; limited vocabulary	choice of words very limited
sentences are complete, fluent, and varied	most sentences are complete and varied	many sentences are complete; generally varied	incomplete sentences; little variety	incomplete sentences; no variety
shows excellent control of writing conventions	shows very good control of writing conventions	shows fairly good control of writing conventions	shows frequent errors in writing conventions	shows many serious errors in writing conventions

■ ■ ■ ■ ■ Writing Scoring Rubrics: Narrative Writing ■ ■ ■ ■ ■ ■ ■ ■ ■ ■ ■ ■ ■ ■ ■

Benchmark Test Teacher's Manual

Writing Scoring Rubrics: Narrative Writing

4-Point Scoring Rubric

4	3	2	1
narrative writing is well focused on the topic	narrative writing is focused on the topic	narrative writing may stray from the topic	narrative writing is not focused on the topic
contains clear ideas	most ideas are clear	some ideas may be unclear	ideas are unclear
logically organized; uses transitions	logically organized; uses some transitions	little organization; may be few or no transitions	unorganized; no transitions
voice is engaging; well suited to purpose and audience	voice is fairly strong; suited to purpose and audience	slight evidence of voice; may be poorly suited to purpose or audience	weak voice; no sense of audience or purpose
demonstrates varied, precise word choice	generally demonstrates varied, precise word choice	choice of words limited	choice of words very limited
sentences are complete, fluent, and varied	most sentences are complete and varied	many incomplete sentences; little variety	mostly incomplete sentences; no variety
shows excellent control of writing conventions	shows very good control of writing conventions	shows frequent errors in writing conventions	shows many serious errors in writing conventions

3-Point Scoring Rubric

3	2	1
narrative writing is well focused on the topic	narrative writing is generally focused on the topic	narrative writing is not focused on the topic
contains clear ideas	ideas are sometimes unclear	ideas are unclear
logically organized; uses transitions	logically organized with lapses; transitions need improvement	unorganized; no transitions
voice is engaging; well suited to purpose and audience	voice comes through fairly well; may not suit purpose or audience	weak voice; no sense of audience
demonstrates varied, precise word choice	word choice could be more varied, precise	choice of words very limited
sentences are complete, fluent, and varied	some sentences are complete and varied	incomplete sentences; no variety
shows excellent control of writing conventions	shows fair control of writing conventions	shows many serious errors in writing conventions

Writing Scoring Rubrics: Descriptive Writing

6-Point Scoring Rubric					
6	**5**	**4**	**3**	**2**	**1**
descriptive writing is well focused on the topic	descriptive writing is focused on the topic	descriptive writing is generally focused on the topic	descriptive writing may stray from the topic	descriptive writing is minimally related to the topic	descriptive writing is not focused on the topic
contains clear ideas	most ideas are clear	ideas are generally clear	ideas may be somewhat unclear	ideas are often unclear	ideas are unclear
logically organized; uses transitions	logically organized; uses some transitions	logically organized with some lapses; has transitions	somewhat organized; may lack transitions	minimally organized; no transitions	unorganized; no transitions
voice is engaging; well suited to purpose and audience	voice comes through well; suited to purpose and audience	voice comes through occasionally; suited to purpose and audience	voice uneven; not always suited to purpose or audience	slight evidence of voice; little sense of purpose or audience	weak voice; no sense of purpose or audience
precise, vivid language paints strong pictures	generally demonstrates varied, precise word choice	often demonstrates varied, precise word choice	word choice could be more varied, precise	poor choice of words; limited vocabulary	limited vocabulary
sentences are complete, fluent, and varied	most sentences are complete and varied	many sentences are complete and varied	some incomplete sentences; little variety	sentences are incomplete; show little or no variety	gross errors in sentence structure; no variety
shows excellent control of writing conventions	shows very good control of writing conventions	shows good control of writing conventions	shows fair control of writing conventions	shows frequent errors in writing conventions	shows many serious errors in writing conventions

5-Point Scoring Rubric				
5	**4**	**3**	**2**	**1**
descriptive writing is well focused on the topic	descriptive writing is focused on the topic	descriptive writing is generally focused on the topic	descriptive writing strays from the topic	descriptive writing is not focused on the topic
contains clear ideas	most ideas are clear	ideas are generally clear	many ideas are unclear	ideas are unclear
logically organized; uses transitions	logically organized; uses some transitions	logically organized with some lapses; transitions weak	little organization; few or no transitions	unorganized; no transitions
voice is engaging; well suited to purpose and audience	voice is fairly engaging; suited to purpose and audience	voice comes through occasionally; may not suit purpose or audience	voice comes through rarely; poorly suited to purpose or audience	weak voice; no sense of audience or purpose
demonstrates varied, precise word choice	generally demonstrates varied, precise word choice	word choice could be more varied, precise	poor word choice; limited vocabulary	word choice very limited
sentences are complete, fluent, and varied	most sentences are complete and varied	many sentences are complete; generally varied	incomplete sentences; little variety	incomplete sentences; no variety
shows excellent control of writing conventions	shows very good control of writing conventions	shows fairly good control of writing conventions	shows frequent errors in writing conventions	shows many serious errors in writing conventions

Benchmark Test Teacher's Manual

Writing Scoring Rubrics: Descriptive Writing

4-Point Scoring Rubric

4	3	2	1
descriptive writing is well focused on the topic	descriptive writing is focused on the topic	descriptive writing may stray from the topic	descriptive writing is not focused on the topic
contains clear ideas	most ideas are clear	some ideas may be unclear	ideas are unclear
logically organized; uses transitions	logically organized; uses some transitions	little organization; may be few or no transitions	unorganized; no transitions
voice is engaging; well suited to purpose and audience	voice is fairly engaging; suited to purpose and audience	slight evidence of voice; may be poorly suited to audience or purpose	weak voice; no sense of audience or purpose
demonstrates varied, precise word choice	generally demonstrates varied, precise word choice	choice of words limited	word choice very limited
sentences are complete, fluent, and varied	most sentences are complete and varied	many incomplete sentences; little variety	mostly incomplete sentences; no variety
shows excellent control of writing conventions	shows very good control of writing conventions	shows frequent errors in writing conventions	shows many serious errors in writing conventions

3-Point Scoring Rubric

3	2	1
descriptive writing is well focused on the topic	descriptive writing is generally focused on the topic	descriptive writing is not focused on the topic
contains clear ideas	ideas are sometimes unclear	ideas are unclear
logically organized; uses transitions	logically organized with lapses; transitions need improvement	unorganized; no transitions
voice is engaging; well suited to purpose and audience	voice comes through fairly well; may not suit purpose or audience	weak voice; no sense of purpose or audience
demonstrates varied, precise word choice	word choice could be more varied, precise	choice of words very limited
sentences are complete, fluent, and varied	some sentences are complete and varied	incomplete sentences; no variety
shows excellent control of writing conventions	shows fair control of writing conventions	shows many serious errors in writing conventions

Writing Scoring Rubrics: Expository Writing

6-Point Scoring Rubric

6	5	4	3	2	1
expository writing is well focused on the topic	expository writing is focused on the topic	expository writing is generally focused on the topic	expository writing may stray from the topic	expository writing is minimally related to the topic	expository writing is not focused on the topic
contains clear ideas	most ideas are clear	ideas are generally clear	ideas may be somewhat unclear	ideas are often unclear	ideas are unclear
logically organized; uses transitions	logically organized; uses some transitions	logically organized with some lapses; has transitions	little organization; may lack transitions	minimally organized; no transitions	unorganized; no transitions
voice is engaging; well suited to purpose and audience	voice comes through well; suited to purpose and audience	voice comes through occasionally; suited to purpose and audience	voice uneven; not always suited to purpose or audience	slight evidence of voice; little sense of purpose or audience	weak voice; no sense of purpose or audience
demonstrates varied, precise word choice	generally demonstrates varied, precise word choice	often demonstrates varied, precise word choice	word choice could be more varied, precise	poor choice of words; limited vocabulary	limited vocabulary
sentences are complete, fluent, and varied	most sentences are complete and varied	many sentences are complete and varied	some incomplete sentences; little variety	sentences are incomplete; show little or no variety	gross errors in sentence structure; no variety
shows excellent control of writing conventions	shows very good control of writing conventions	shows good control of writing conventions	shows fair control of writing conventions	shows frequent errors in writing conventions	shows many serious errors in writing conventions

5-Point Scoring Rubric

5	4	3	2	1
expository writing is well focused on the topic	expository writing is focused on the topic	expository writing is generally focused on the topic	expository writing strays from the topic	expository writing is not focused on the topic
contains clear ideas	most ideas are clear	ideas are generally clear	many ideas are unclear	ideas are unclear
logically organized; uses transitions	logically organized; uses some transitions	logically organized with some lapses; transitions weak	little organization; few or no transitions	unorganized; no transitions
voice is engaging; well suited to purpose and audience	voice is fairly engaging; suited to purpose and audience	voice comes through occasionally; may not suit purpose or audience	voice comes through rarely; poorly suited to purpose or audience	weak voice; no sense of audience or purpose
demonstrates varied, precise word choice	generally demonstrates varied, precise word choice	word choice could be more varied, precise	poor word choice; limited vocabulary	word choice very limited
sentences are complete, fluent, and varied	most sentences are complete and varied	many sentences are complete; generally varied	incomplete sentences; little variety	incomplete sentences; no variety
shows excellent control of writing conventions	shows very good control of writing conventions	shows fairly good control of writing conventions	shows frequent errors in writing conventions	shows many serious errors in writing conventions

Writing Scoring Rubrics: Expository Writing

4-Point Scoring Rubric

4	3	2	1
expository writing is well focused on the topic	expository writing is focused on the topic	expository writing may stray from the topic	expository writing is not focused on the topic
contains clear ideas	most ideas are clear	some ideas may be unclear	ideas are unclear
logically organized; uses transitions	logically organized; uses some transitions	little organization; may be few or no transitions	unorganized; no transitions
voice is engaging; well suited to purpose and audience	voice is fairly engaging; suited to purpose and audience	slight evidence of voice; may be poorly suited to audience or purpose	weak voice; no sense of audience or purpose
demonstrates varied, precise word choice	generally demonstrates varied, precise word choice	choice of words limited	word choice very limited
sentences are complete, fluent, and varied	most sentences are complete and varied	many incomplete sentences; little variety	mostly incomplete sentences; no variety
shows excellent control of writing conventions	shows very good control of writing conventions	shows frequent errors in writing conventions	shows many serious errors in writing conventions

3-Point Scoring Rubric

3	2	1
expository writing is well focused on the topic	expository writing is generally focused on the topic	expository writing is not focused on the topic
contains clear ideas	ideas are sometimes unclear	ideas are unclear
logically organized; uses transitions	logically organized with lapses; transitions need improvement	unorganized; no transitions
voice is engaging; well suited to purpose and audience	voice comes through fairly well; may not suit purpose or audience	weak voice; no sense of purpose or audience
demonstrates varied, precise word choice	word choice could be more varied, precise	choice of words very limited
sentences are complete, fluent, and varied	some sentences are complete and varied	incomplete sentences; no variety
shows excellent control of writing conventions	shows fair control of writing conventions	shows many serious errors in writing conventions

Writing Scoring Rubrics: Persuasive Writing

6-Point Scoring Rubric

6	5	4	3	2	1
persuasive writing is well focused on the topic	persuasive writing is focused on the topic	persuasive writing is generally focused on the topic	persuasive writing is generally focused but may stray from the topic	persuasive writing is minimally related to the topic	persuasive writing is not focused on the topic
contains clear ideas	most ideas are clear	ideas are generally clear	ideas may be somewhat unclear	ideas are often unclear	ideas are unclear
presents reasons in order; uses transitions	presents reasons in some order; uses some transitions	presents most reasons in order; has transitions	reasons may not be in proper order; may lack transitions	reasons are not in order; no transitions	reasons, if any, are not in order; no transitions
voice is engaging; well suited to purpose and audience	voice comes through well; suited to purpose and audience	voice comes through occasionally; suited to purpose and audience	voice uneven; not always suited to purpose or audience	slight evidence of voice; little sense of audience or purpose	weak voice; no sense of purpose or audience
demonstrates precise, persuasive wording	generally demonstrates precise, persuasive word choice	often demonstrates precise, persuasive word choice	word choice is not always precise or persuasive	poor choice of words; not very persuasive	limited vocabulary; fails to persuade
sentences are complete, fluent, and varied	most sentences are complete and varied	many sentences are complete and varied	some incomplete sentences; little variety	sentences are incomplete; show little or no variety	gross errors in sentence structure; no variety
shows excellent control of writing conventions	shows very good control of writing conventions	shows good control of writing conventions	shows fair control of writing conventions	shows frequent errors in writing conventions	shows many serious errors in writing conventions

5-Point Scoring Rubric

5	4	3	2	1
persuasive writing is well focused on the topic	persuasive writing is focused on the topic	persuasive writing is generally focused on the topic	persuasive writing strays from the topic	persuasive writing is not focused on the topic
contains clear ideas	most ideas are clear	ideas are generally clear	many ideas are unclear	ideas are unclear
presents reasons in order; uses transitions	presents reasons in some order; uses some transitions	presents most reasons in order; transitions weak	reasons are not in order; few or no transitions	reasons, if any, are not in order; no transitions
voice is engaging; well suited to purpose and audience	voice is fairly engaging; suited to purpose and audience	voice comes through occasionally; may not suit purpose or audience	voice comes through rarely; poorly suited to audience or purpose	weak voice; no sense of audience or purpose
demonstrates precise, persuasive wording	generally demonstrates precise, persuasive word choice	word choice could be more precise, persuasive	word choice limited; not persuasive	word choice very limited; fails to persuade
sentences are complete, fluent, and varied	most sentences are complete and varied	many sentences are complete; generally varied	incomplete sentences; little variety	incomplete sentences; no variety
shows excellent control of writing conventions	shows very good control of writing conventions	shows fairly good control of writing conventions	shows frequent errors in writing conventions	shows many serious errors in writing conventions

Benchmark Test Teacher's Manual

Writing Scoring Rubrics: Persuasive Writing

4-Point Scoring Rubric			
4	**3**	**2**	**1**
persuasive writing is well focused on the topic	persuasive writing is focused on the topic	persuasive writing may stray from the topic	persuasive writing is not focused on the topic
contains clear ideas	most ideas are clear	some ideas may be unclear	ideas are unclear
presents reasons in order; uses transitions	presents reasons in some order; uses some transitions	reasons may not be in order; may be few or no transitions	reasons, if any, are not in order; no transitions
voice is engaging; well suited to purpose and audience	voice is fairly engaging; suited to purpose and audience	slight evidence of voice; may be poorly suited to purpose or audience	weak voice; no sense of audience or purpose
demonstrates precise, persuasive wording	generally demonstrates precise, persuasive word choice	choice of words limited; not very persuasive	word choice very limited; fails to persuade
sentences are complete, fluent, and varied	most sentences are complete and varied	many incomplete sentences; little variety	many incomplete sentences; no variety
shows excellent control of writing conventions	shows very good control of writing conventions	shows frequent errors in writing conventions	shows many serious errors in writing conventions

3-Point Scoring Rubric		
3	**2**	**1**
persuasive writing is well focused on the topic	persuasive writing is generally focused on the topic	persuasive writing is not focused on the topic
contains clear ideas	ideas are sometimes unclear	ideas are unclear
logically organized; presents reasons in order	logically organized with lapses; presents most reasons in order	unorganized; reasons, if any, are not in order
voice is engaging; well suited to purpose and audience	voice comes through fairly well; may not suit audience or purpose	weak voice; no sense of audience or purpose
demonstrates precise, persuasive word choice	word choice could be more precise, persuasive	choice of words very limited; fails to persuade
sentences are complete, fluent, and varied	some sentences are complete and varied	incomplete sentences; no variety
shows excellent control of writing conventions	shows fair control of writing conventions	shows many serious errors in writing conventions

Using an Evaluation Chart

Use the Evaluation Charts beginning on page T31 to score the Unit Benchmark Tests and the End-of-Year Benchmark Test. To score one of these tests use the following procedure:

1. Make a copy of the appropriate Evaluation Chart for each student.

2. To score Reading – Parts 1–3, circle the score for each item on the Evaluation Chart. Multiple-choice questions are scored 0 (incorrect) or 1 (correct). Constructed-response questions are scored 0, 1, or 2 points. Use the answer key for the test you are scoring and the Constructed-Response Scoring Rubric on page T11 to help you score the Reading parts of the test.

3. Find the student's total score for Reading – Parts 1–3 by adding the individual scores for all items.

4. Use the formula on the Evaluation Chart to find the percentage score for Reading – Parts 1–3 by dividing the total *obtained* score by the total *possible* score and then multiplying the quotient by 100.

5. To score Writing – Part 4, identify the type of writing suggested in the prompt and choose one of the four Writing Scoring Rubrics for that type of writing. Read the student's writing and score each composition on a scale from 1 to 6, 1 to 5, 1 to 4, or 1 to 3.

6. Mark the student's Writing score on the Evaluation Chart. Add any notes or observations about the writing that may be helpful to you and the student in later instruction.

INTERPRETING TEST RESULTS

A student's score on a Benchmark Test provides only one look at the student's progress and should be interpreted in conjunction with other assessments and the teacher's observations. However, a low score on one or both parts of a Benchmark Test probably indicates a need for closer review of the student's performance and perhaps additional instruction.

Regrouping for Instruction

The Benchmark Tests can help you make regrouping decisions. In Grade 6 there are opputunities for regrouping at the end of Units 2, 3, 4, and 6. Depending on each student's progress, teachers may prefer to regroup more or less frequently.

Students who score 65% or below on the multiple-choice items of the Comprehension and Vocabulary sections of the Benchmark Tests and who typically demonstrate unsatisfactory work on assignments and in classroom discussions would benefit from being in the Strategic Intervention reading group for the next unit of instruction.

Students who score between 66% and 90% on the multiple-choice items of the Comprehension and Vocabulary sections of the Benchmark Tests and who meet other criteria, such as consistently satisfactory work on assignments and in classroom discussions, likely belong in the On-Level reading group for the next unit of instruction. Students in the low end of that range should be observed carefully and may need on-going assistance, extra instruction, and opportunities for further practice, just as students in the Strategic Intervention group do. Students in the upper end of that range should receive their instruction and practice with on-level materials, but they may need extra challenge and enrichment, just as students in the Advanced reading group do.

Students who score 91% or above on the multiple-choice items of the Comprehension and Vocabulary sections of the Benchmark Tests and who meet other criteria, such as consistently excellent performance on assigned paperwork and in classroom discussions, are capable of work in the Advanced reading group for the next unit of instruction. They should be given multiple opportunities to engage in enrichment activities and real-world investigations.

Further Analysis of Results

Each Reading (Parts 1–3) item on an Evaluation Chart is linked to a tested skill and a Common Core State Standard. By identifying which items the student answered incorrectly and referring to the list of tested skills, you may be able to determine specific skills or areas in which the student needs additional help. For example, if the student answers six questions incorrectly and several involve literary elements such as plot and character, you may want to plan additional instruction for the student in this area. While the Benchmark Tests do not provide sufficient context coverage of individual skills to be truly "diagnostic," students' performance patterns can often provide useful clues as to particular strengths and weaknesses.

Grading: For more information on how to use a writing assessment scale as an element in determining classroom grades, refer to the "Grading Writing" section of the *Assessment Handbook*.

ASSISTING ENGLISH LANGUAGE LEARNERS

While the Benchmark Tests provide teachers with a way to measure students' progress on a unit-by-unit basis, Benchmark Tests also provide an opportunity for teachers to help English language learners become familiar with the linguistic patterns and structures they will encounter while taking state tests. The format of the Benchmark Tests is similar to the format of the state tests, with similar direction lines, question stems, answer formats, and markings to "stop" and "go on."

Among assessment tools, standardized tests cause teachers of English language learners the most concern. State tests, considered "high stakes," may be used to evaluate the effectiveness of the curriculum, the teacher, or the instructional approach. They are used to evaluate students' overall progress. High-stakes tests are typically designed and normed for proficient speakers of English. By providing opportunities for English language learners to become familiar with the formats and language of the Benchmark Tests, teachers assist students in obtaining results that reflect students' learning of the content rather than their aptitude for comprehending test language and formats.

Teachers can use specific strategies to prepare English language learners for assessment. Using these strategies on the Benchmark Tests will increase students' comfort levels and success with assessment tools such as the state tests.

Testing Strategies for All English Language Learners
Provide Accommodations for Students' Success

Any accommodations appropriate for English language learners should address students' linguistic needs, either directly or indirectly. As you consider accommodations for students taking the Benchmark Tests, remember that when the state tests are given, no special accommodations are allowed. Therefore, as you make accommodations for English language learners, keep in mind that the ultimate goal is for these students to handle mainstream testing settings, terminology, and instruction. Any accommodations that you provide should be considered stepping stones to students' eventual successful encounter with mainstream testing conditions.

1. **Simplify and clarify directions.** Providing instructions in simplified formats can reduce the language load for English language learners and help them focus solely on the task and content for the specific question(s). A good rule of thumb is to match the language used with the test to the language used with instruction. Students benefit from your replacing complex English words with simpler English words that they are already familiar with or can grasp more easily. However, it is never appropriate to translate test directions into students' home languages. This practice will not benefit students when they encounter state tests. (*See below* **A Word of Caution.**) However, you may ask students to restate directions in their own words so you are sure they understand them.

2. **Provide a setting consistent with the instructional setting.** Administering tests in an alternate, smaller, even one-on-one, setting can allow for verbal scaffolding and provide English language learners with a setting that is comfortable and familiar to them. Be sure that the alternate setting is a setting with which students are familiar. Move students to mainstream testing settings when you feel they are ready.

3. **Consider timing.** Provide additional testing time and allow frequent or extended breaks during testing. On the Benchmark Tests, for example, students may benefit from a break between the two Comprehension selection/item sets or after the Comprehension and Vocabulary sections before moving on to the Writing Conventions section. The Writing sections are rigorous for students. Consider completing these portions on a different day or after a significant break. Keep in mind, however, that while this type of accommodation is one that is most often used for English language learners in mainstream classrooms, it is more important to be sure that students are receiving the necessary linguistic support in English.

4. **Provide dictionaries.** Allow the use of bilingual, word-for-word translation dictionaries as an accommodation for students who are able to use them effectively.

A Word of Caution: In providing accommodations to students, it is important not to compromise the intent of the assessment. It is never appropriate to translate into students' native languages or read aloud in English selections and questions. These practices alter the constructs of the assessments. The reading comprehension assessments, for example, are designed to measure both word recognition and understanding, so translating or reading the selections to students actually changes the intent of the tests.

Following the administration of the assessments, it is important to note which accommodations were used for English language learners and to interpret scores with that information in mind. As students progress in their English language skills and become more comfortable with testing, it is important to reconsider accommodations that were provided on previous tests.

Familiarize Students with Academic Language and Test Language

The Benchmark Tests use routine terminology and formats that are designed to mirror the experience of taking state tests. Helping students improve their understanding and use of academic language is an essential way to prepare students for assessment. The practice of "teaching to the test" is often criticized—and rightfully so—but helping English language learners understand the language and formats of tests and other assessment instruments levels the playing field for these students, allowing them to demonstrate what they've learned about the content, rather than struggling with the test language and formats. All students, but especially English language learners, must be taught test-taking strategies and must build background about the language and procedures of taking tests. **What strategies can you explicitly offer to students to prepare for assessment?**

1. Focus on Academic English and Meaningful Oral Language Experiences
Many English language learners may quickly master *social* English, the conversational language skills and conventions used in everyday interactions with classmates. These same learners, however, frequently encounter difficulty with the *academic* English found on formal assessments. Students may also have gaps in understanding between oral and written English. The structure of academic English is complex, e.g., fiction and nonfiction text structures, paragraph organization, and syntax, including prepositional phrases, introductory clauses, and pronoun references. There are structural analysis constraints at the word, sentence, paragraph, and text levels.

Development of academic language is one of the primary sources of difficulty for English language learners at all ages and grades while also being fundamental to all students' success. The vocabulary of academic English consists of specialized meanings of common words, abstract concepts, multiple-meaning words, and words based on Latin and Greek roots. As students read test selections, they may encounter unfamiliar topics and concepts. Recognize that it takes years for students to master academic English, but that you can help them make progress on the way. Highlight and discuss routinely the *academic* language, vocabulary, syntax, and narrative and expository text structures encountered in textbooks and trade books.

Remember that academic English is not another name for "standard English." Academic English is the special form of English that is used in the classroom and in written texts. The grammatical constructions, words, and rhetorical conventions are not often used in everyday spoken language. The home language does *not* have to be English in order for students to benefit from experiences in using academic language. If it proves helpful, students may be encouraged to connect what they know in their home languages to what they are learning about academic English.

Provide students with experiences with academic language by reading to them and discussing readings, instructional activities, and experiences. Draw students into instructional conversations focused on the language they encounter in their school texts and other materials to show students how language works. Provide students with ample opportunities to use the language of texts—and tests—in speaking and in writing. Provide regular opportunities for meaningful oral language experiences in which English language learners participate in discussion of important topics and perform the activities required on tests, such as explaining, describing, comparing, and stating and supporting opinions. Encourage them to use vocabulary that will support academic language development in increased opportunities for structured academic talk.

2. Focus on Test Directions

Help students understand phrases such as "make heavy dark marks" and "fill the circle completely" that are often used in test directions. When possible, model tasks and provide verbal directions in simpler, more common English words. Be explicit in your teaching, using the following examples as a guide.

- **Make heavy dark marks that fill the circle completely.**

- **If you erase a grid circle, do not redraw it.**

- **Do not make any stray marks on this answer sheet.**

For the directions above, talk about the word *heavy* and its different meanings. Be sure students understand that here it means "dark." Explain that a *grid circle* is simply a "circle," *redraw* means "draw again," and *stray marks* means "marks in other places." Model and gesture how to follow the directions: *I use this answer sheet, or page. I find the number of the question in the booklet, or book, and I match the number in the booklet to the number on the sheet, or page, like this. Then I find the circle for the letter of the correct answer and make it all dark, or black, with my pencil. I do not make other marks on the page.* Be sure students can fill in the test form clearly
and neatly.

3. Focus on Terminology and Strategies

Think about terms that will make the most sense to students as you teach. Instead of using the words *directions, test,* and *fill,* for example, you might use common cognates such as *instructions, exam,* and *mark,* which translate to most Romance languages (i.e., in Spanish: *instrucciones, examen,* and *marca*). However, move students to the original test words as soon as possible.

Preteach the "language of tests" encountered in directions and test items, including:

Question words, such as: *who, what, which, where, when, why, how, and what kind*

Emphasis words, such as: *best, better, first, last, not, except, probably, major, main, mainly, both, neither, either, same, different, begin, end, most, mostly,* and *least*

Action words, such as: *explain, describe, compare and contrast,* and *discuss.*

Words such as *both* and *not* may seem simple, but their uses in test questions often prove otherwise. English language learners need help in seeing how such words frame and constrain ideas expressed in sentences in which they appear.

Throughout the year, students need robust vocabulary instruction in English for additional common test words and phrases such as *test form, test booklet, answer sheet, mark the space, best describes, author, reader, purpose, paragraph, selection, article, passage, composition, essay, writing prompt, details, events, results, according to, alike, opposite of, synonym, antonym, clue word, homonym, statements of fact and opinion, include, occur, present in, represent, resolve, refer to, replace, valid comparison, important generalization, base your answer on,* and *support your answer.* Examine the tests for other words and phrases that are important for students to learn.

Familiarize students with basic test formats such as the lettering of multiple-choice options, underlining or italicizing of key words and parts of words, cloze sentences, and writing-prompt boxes, so that they develop skills in locating key information. Use released tests or models of tests, providing students with plenty of practice in test formats. Be explicit in your instruction, using the following examples as a guide.

Read this thesaurus entry for *debris.* **Then do Number 31.**

debris *n.*	**1.** ruin, remains, wreck **2.** pieces, parts **3.** junk, trash

31   **Which word from the thesaurus entry would best replace**
debris **in the following sentence?**

> *The lot adjacent to Marcie's building had long*
> *been littered with weeds and* debris, *including a*
> *pile of cardboard boxes and old tires.*

A   ruin

B   wreck

C   parts

D   junk

Explain the test item type and format: *Some test questions use a thesaurus entry to ask me about a word in a sentence from a selection. The tested word is in italics, a kind of type that has slanted letters. A thesaurus entry shows different words that can be used to mean about the same thing. Each word has a little different meaning, although their meanings are very close. I need to choose the word that could best take the place of the tested word in the sentence shown. The correct answer has the same meaning as the tested word, as it is used in the sentence from the selection.* Model how to complete this type of question.

29   **What are the guide words for the page in the dictionary on**
which the word *succession* **is found?**

A   submit—successful

B   stomach—subtract

C   square—stable

D   submarine—such

Explain the test item type and format: *This question tests what I know about the dictionary. I have to know that a dictionary gives meanings of words, and words are arranged alphabetically. Every page in a dictionary has words at the top. They're called "guide words." These words are the first and last word on the page, and they save me time when I'm looking for a word. I don't have to look at every word on the page. For this question I have to decide where the word in italics, or slanted letters, would fit in the dictionary. Between which pair of words would I find it?*

PROMPT

At one time or another, each of us has helped others and has received help from others. In an essay, briefly describe one experience when you helped someone and one experience when you received someone's help. Then compare and contrast the two experiences in terms of how you benefited from each.

Explain the test format: *Some tests ask me to write a story or an essay. At the top of the page is an instruction box, or writing prompt. First I read the instructions in the box to learn what to write about. I have to read all the instructions very carefully, because there may be several steps I have to follow. The next two pages have lines for me to write on.* Explain also the "Checklist for Writers" box: *These are questions I read to myself and answer as I check over my essay to make sure it's just the way I want it.*

Model test-taking strategies for students. Help them use their emerging familiarity with vocabulary and basic language structures in English to select the best answer and eliminate multiple-choice options. Teach students the logic of test questions. Show students, for example, that the question "Which of the following is *not* a sentence?" entails that all of the listed options except one *are* sentences. Be sure to teach students the types of reading comprehension questions they may encounter on tests. Use released test items or models of test items to provide students with plenty of practice in question types and the test-taking strategies you have taught them. Be explicit in your instruction, using the following examples as a guide.

1 **Which of the following <u>events</u> occurred <u>first</u> in the story?**

A Lexie <u>called</u> the <u>Red Cross</u>.

B Lexie <u>complained to her brothers</u>.

C Lexie took a <u>babysitting</u> class.

D Lexie found out about <u>disaster relief</u>.

Model a test-taking strategy for students—underlining key words in the question and answers: *I read the whole selection carefully before I try to answer the questions. What if I can't remember something? Do I guess? No. I can make lines under the important words in the question and answers to help me. What are the important words in the question?* Events *and* first. *So, I need to find which event came first in the story. I am not sure. What do I do? I can underline important words in the answers. Then I can search for these words in the selection. I can see where they come in the story. Are they at the beginning, middle, or end of the story? This will help me choose the correct answer.*

22 **What was the author's purpose in writing this selection?**

F to entertain readers with details of a vacation

G to persuade people to take more pictures

H to explain how to build a sand city

J to express an opinion about family vacations

Model a test-taking strategy for students—identifying the author's purpose through the main idea and genre of the selection: *I read the whole selection carefully before I try to answer the questions. This question asks why the author wrote the selection. That is tied to the main idea and genre, or type, of the selection. What is the selection mostly about? A boy's vacation. What kind of selection is it? A fictional, or made-up, letter a boy wrote to his grandmother. Now I read the answer choices. The first answer seems correct, but I am not sure so I look at the other answers and try to eliminate, or get rid of, a few of them. I look at answer* **G.** *Does the author try to get readers to take more pictures? No. He talks about one picture of the sand city. It is not a persuasive essay, trying to get readers to do something. So,* **G** *is not correct. I look at answer* **H.** *Does the author give a lot of details about how to build a sand city? The boy tells what the sand city looked like but he did not give directions for making it. It is not a how-to selection. So,* **H** *is not correct. I look at answer* **J.** *Does the author express an opinion about vacations? The boy tells in the letter how much he liked his vacation, but that is not the same as the author's opinion about vacations. So,* **J** *is not correct. I look again at answer* **F.** *Does the selection entertain readers with details of a vacation? Yes. The selection is a fictional, made-up, letter from a boy to his grandma about a fun vacation. The author wrote this selection to entertain me, or make me enjoy reading the letter.*

PROMPT

In <u>both</u> selections, people and characters build something. <u>Describe the materials</u> each set of builders <u>used</u> and some <u>challenges</u> each faced while building. Give details or examples from both selections to explain your answer.

Explain how to prepare for a constructed-response question: *I read both selections carefully before I try to answer this question. In this part of the test, I have to write. I read the question in the box carefully. It tells me I must think about both selections. I underline the important words in the question to help me understand what I am supposed to do. The word "describe" means "tell about." I have to tell about the materials the builders used to make the sand city and the Brooklyn Bridge. The question also asks me to tell about the challenges. These are things that happened, or events, that made the jobs hard for the builders. The question says to use details or examples from both selections to explain my answer. What does that mean? That means that I can't just list the building materials and challenges. I have to give information about them. I can look at the selections again to help me think of what to write about.*

Model for students how to read the test itself. Proficient English readers may benefit from strategies such as reading the test question and answer options first and then skimming the selection to find information that will help them select the correct answer to the question. English language learners are not served well by this option. They need to read and understand the selection carefully and then consider how to answer the questions asked. Model this type of test-taking strategy for students as you think aloud and explain the process.

Summarize test formats and strategies for students. Consider making a T-chart to show examples of the question types that students may find on tests. If your T-chart is large enough to be a wall chart, include examples of each type of item from released tests and model tests on the chart. Explain what the structures are and what they ask test-takers to do (or ask students to explain as you teach various strategies).

Evaluation Chart: Grade 6 – Unit 1 Benchmark Test

Student Name _____   Date _____

Reading – Parts 1–3

Item	Tested Skill	Item Type*	Common Core State Standard	Score (circle one)
Reading – Part 1: Comprehension				
1.	Literary elements: character	I	Literature 3.	0 1
2.	Literary elements: character	C	Literature 3.	0 1
3.	Compare and contrast	C	Literature 1.	0 1
4.	Literary elements: character	I	Literature 3.	0 1
5.	Literary elements: setting	I	Literature 5.	0 1
6.	Literary elements: setting	C	Literature 5.	0 1
7.	Cause and effect	I	Literature 1.	0 1
8.	Literary elements: plot	C	Literature 3.	0 1
9.	Literary elements: character	I	Literature 3.	0 1
10.	Literary elements: character	L	Literature 3.	0 1
11.	Compare and contrast	C	Literature 3.	0 1
A.	Constructed-response text-to-world connection		Writing 2.	0 1 2
12.	Main idea and details	I	Informational Text 2.	0 1
13.	Cause and effect	I	Informational Text 2.	0 1
14.	Fact and opinion	C	Informational Text 8.	0 1
15.	Compare and contrast	C	Informational Text 8.	0 1
16.	Graphic sources	C	Informational Text 7.	0 1
17.	Fact and opinion	C	Informational Text 8.	0 1
18.	Graphic sources	L	Informational Text 7.	0 1
19.	Author's purpose	C	Informational Text 8.	0 1
20.	Fact and opinion	C	Informational Text 8.	0 1
21.	Author's purpose	C	Informational Text 8.	0 1
22.	Cause and effect	L	Informational Text 1.	0 1
B.	Constructed-response text-to-text connection		Writing 2.	0 1 2
Reading – Part 2: Vocabulary				
23.	Word structure: suffixes		Language 4.a.	0 1
24.	Word structure: Greek and Latin roots		Language 4.b.	0 1
25.	Word structure: endings		Language 4.	0 1
26.	Word structure: endings		Language 4.	0 1
27.	Word structure: suffixes		Language 5.	0 1
28.	Word structure: Greek and Latin roots		Language 4.b.	0 1
29.	Context clues: unfamiliar words		Language 4.a.	0 1

Reading – Part 2: Vocabulary (continued)				
30.	Thesaurus: synonyms	Language 4.c.	0	1
31.	Thesaurus: synonyms	Language 4.c.	0	1
32.	Context clues: unfamiliar words	Language 4.a.	0	1
Reading – Part 3: Writing Conventions				
33.	Common and proper nouns	Language 2.	0	1
34.	Common and proper nouns	Language 2.	0	1
35.	Imperative sentences	Language 1.	0	1
36.	Subjects and predicates	Language 1.	0	1
37.	Subjects and predicates	Language 1.	0	1
38.	Compound and complex sentences	Language 1.	0	1
39.	Independent and dependent clauses	Language 1.	0	1
40.	Compound and complex sentences	Language 1.	0	1
Student's Reading Total Score/Total Possible Score _____			**/44**	

*L = literal   I = inferential   C = critical analysis

Reading — Parts 1–3 percentage score: _____ ÷ 44 = _____ × 100 = _____%
                    (student's total score)   (percentage score)

Writing – Part 4	Common Core State Standards
Writing Score (complete one) _____/6 _____/5 _____/4 _____/3	
Notes/Observations:	Writing 3. Writing 4. Writing 10. Language 1. Language 2.

Student Name _____ Date _____

Reading – Parts 1–3

Item	Tested Skill	Item Type*	Common Core State Standard	Score (circle one)
Reading – Part 1: Comprehension				
1.	Main idea and details	I	Informational Text 2.	0 1
2.	Generalize	C	Informational Text 1.	0 1
3.	Compare and contrast	C	Informational Text 1.	0 1
4.	Main idea and details	L	Informational Text 2.	0 1
5.	Graphic sources	C	Informational Text 7.	0 1
6.	Compare and contrast	C	Informational Text 1.	0 1
7.	Main idea and details	L	Informational Text 2.	0 1
8.	Graphic sources	C	Informational Text 1.	0 1
9.	Sequence	C	Informational Text 2.	0 1
10.	Main idea and details	C	Informational Text 2.	0 1
11.	Sequence	I	Informational Text 5.	0 1
A.	Constructed-response text-to-world connection		Writing 2.	0 1 2
12.	Sequence	I	Informational Text 5.	0 1
13.	Sequence	L	Informational Text 6.	0 1
14.	Compare and contrast	C	Informational Text 6.	0 1
15.	Main idea and details	I	Informational Text 2.	0 1
16.	Compare and contrast	L	Informational Text 1.	0 1
17.	Graphic sources	I	Informational Text 7.	0 1
18.	Generalize	C	Informational Text 1.	0 1
19.	Main idea and details	I	Informational Text 2.	0 1
20.	Graphic sources	C	Informational Text 7.	0 1
21.	Generalize	C	Informational Text 1.	0 1
22.	Generalize	C	Informational Text 1.	0 1
B.	Constructed-response text-to-text connection		Writing 2.	0 1 2
Reading – Part 2: Vocabulary				
23.	Context clues: unfamiliar words		Language 4.a.	0 1
24.	Word structure: suffixes		Language 4.	0 1
25.	Word structure: Greek and Latin roots		Language 4.b.	0 1
26.	Dictionary/glossary: unknown words		Language 4.c.	0 1
27.	Word structure: suffixes		Language 4.	0 1
28.	Word structure: suffixes		Language 4.	0 1
29.	Dictionary/glossary: unknown words		Language 4.c.	0 1

- - - - - - - - Evaluation Chart: Grade 6 — Unit 2 Benchmark Test - - - - - - - - - - -

Reading – Part 2: Vocabulary (continued)			
30.	Dictionary/glossary: unknown words	Language 4.c.	0 1
31.	Dictionary/glossary: unknown words	Language 4.c.	0 1
32.	Word structure: Greek and Latin roots	Language 4.b.	0 1
Student's Regrouping Multiple-Choice Score/Total Possible Score			_____/32
Reading – Part 3: Writing Conventions			
33.	Past, present, and future tenses	Language 1.	0 1
34.	Action and linking	Language 1.	0 1
35.	Regular and irregular plural nouns	Language 1.	0 1
36.	Subject-verb agreement	Language 1.	0 1
37.	Possessive nouns	Language 2.	0 1
38.	Subject-verb agreement	Language 1.	0 1
39.	Regular and irregular plural nouns	Language 1.	0 1
40.	Possessive nouns	Language 2.	0 1
Student's Reading Total Score/Total Possible Score			_____/44

*L = literal   I = inferential   C = critical analysis

Regrouping (Reading — Parts 1–2) percentage score: _____ ÷ 32 = _____ × 100 = _____%
           (student's score)   (percentage score)

Reading — Parts 1–3 percentage score: _____ ÷ 44 = _____ × 100 = _____%
           (student's total score)   (percentage score)

Writing – Part 4	Common Core State Standards
Writing Score (complete one) _____/6 _____/5 _____/4 _____/3	
Notes/Observations:	Writing 2. Writing 4. Writing 10. Language 1. Language 2.

Evaluation Chart: Grade 6 — Unit 3 Benchmark Test

Student Name _____   Date _____

Item	Tested Skill	Item Type*	Common Core State Standard	Score (circle one)
Reading – Parts 1–3				
Reading – Part 1: Comprehension				
1.	Sequence	I	Literature 5.	0 1
2.	Draw conclusions	I	Literature 1.	0 1
3.	Draw conclusions	I	Literature 1.	0 1
4.	Literary elements: plot	C	Literature 3.	0 1
5.	Draw conclusions	I	Literature 1.	0 1
6.	Literary elements: character	I	Literature 3.	0 1
7.	Literary elements: plot	I	Literature 3.	0 1
8.	Literary elements: plot	C	Literature 3.	0 1
9.	Literary elements: character	I	Literature 3.	0 1
10.	Cause and effect	L	Literature 5.	0 1
11.	Sequence	L	Literature 5.	0 1
A.	Constructed-response text-to-world connection		Writing 1.	0 1 2
12.	Generalize	I	Informational Text 1.	0 1
13.	Draw conclusions	I	Informational Text 1.	0 1
14.	Sequence	I	Informational Text 5.	0 1
15.	Cause and effect	L	Informational Text 1.	0 1
16.	Generalize	C	Informational Text 1.	0 1
17.	Cause and effect	I	Informational Text 1.	0 1
18.	Draw conclusions	C	Informational Text 1.	0 1
19.	Sequence	I	Informational Text 5.	0 1
20.	Draw conclusions	I	Informational Text 1.	0 1
21.	Generalize	C	Informational Text 1.	0 1
22.	Generalize	C	Informational Text 1.	0 1
B.	Constructed-response text-to-text connection		Writing 1.	0 1 2
Reading – Part 2: Vocabulary				
23.	Word structure: word endings		Language 4.	0 1
24.	Context clues: antonyms		Language 4.a.	0 1
25.	Context clues: synonyms		Language 4.a.	0 1
26.	Context clues: synonyms		Language 4.a.	0 1
27.	Word structure: suffixes		Language 4.a.	0 1
28.	Word structure: word endings		Language 4.	0 1

– – – – – E v a l u a t i o n   C h a r t :   G r a d e   6   —   U n i t   3   B e n c h m a r k   T e s t – – – – – – –

Reading – Part 2: Vocabulary (continued)			
29.	Word structure: prefixes	Language 4.	0 1
30.	Word structure: prefixes	Language 4.	0 1
31.	Context clues: antonyms	Language 4.a.	0 1
32.	Word structure: suffixes	Language 5.	0 1
Student's Regrouping Multiple-Choice Score/Total Possible Score			_____ /32
Reading – Part 3: Writing Conventions			
33.	Verbs, objects, and subject complements	Language 1.	0 1
34.	Verbs, objects, and subject complements	Language 1.	0 1
35.	Troublesome verbs	Language 1.	0 1
36.	Principal parts of regular verbs	Language 1.	0 1
37.	Troublesome verbs	Language 1.	0 1
38.	Troublesome verbs	Language 1.	0 1
39.	Verbs, objects, and subject complements	Language 1.	0 1
40.	Verbs, objects, and subject complements	Language 1.	0 1
Student's Reading Total Score/Total Possible Score			_____ /44

*L = literal   I = inferential   C = critical analysis

Regrouping (Reading — Parts 1–2) percentage score: _____ ÷ 32 = _____ × 100 = _____ %
                                                    (student's score)   (percentage score)

Reading — Parts 1–3 percentage score: _____ ÷ 44 = _____ × 100 = _____ %
                                      (student's total score)   (percentage score)

Writing – Part 4	
Writing Score (complete one) _____ /6 _____ /5 _____ /4 _____ /3	**Common Core State Standards**
Notes/Observations:	Writing 2. Writing 4. Writing 10. Language 1. Language 2.

Evaluation Chart: Grade 6 — Unit 4 Benchmark Test

Student Name _____ Date _____

Reading – Parts 1–3				
Item	**Tested Skill**	**Item Type***	**Common Core State Standard**	**Score** (circle one)
Reading – Part 1: Comprehension				
1.	Sequence	I	Informational Text 5.	0 1
2.	Cause and effect	C	Informational Text 1.	0 1
3.	Cause and effect	I	Informational Text 3.	0 1
4.	Fact and opinion	C	Informational Text 8.	0 1
5.	Draw conclusions	I	Informational Text 3.	0 1
6.	Main idea and details	I	Informational Text 2.	0 1
7.	Main idea and details	I	Informational Text 2.	0 1
8.	Generalize	I	Informational Text 1.	0 1
9.	Draw conclusions	C	Informational Text 1.	0 1
10.	Author's purpose	C	Informational Text 8.	0 1
11.	Cause and effect	L	Informational Text 3.	0 1
A.	Constructed-response text-to-world connection		Writing 2.	0 1 2
12.	Cause and effect	L	Literature 5.	0 1
13.	Cause and effect	L	Literature 1.	0 1
14.	Sequence	L	Literature 5.	0 1
15.	Sequence	I	Literature 5.	0 1
16.	Cause and effect	C	Literature 1.	0 1
17.	Literary elements: setting	L	Literature 1.	0 1
18.	Literary elements: character	I	Literature 3.	0 1
19.	Compare and contrast	I	Literature 3.	0 1
20.	Author's purpose	C	Literature 6.	0 1
21.	Draw conclusions	I	Literature 3.	0 1
22.	Author's purpose	C	Literature 1.	0 1
B.	Constructed-response text-to-text connection		Writing 2.	0 1 2
Reading – Part 2: Vocabulary				
23.	Context clues: unfamiliar words		Language 4.a.	0 1
24.	Context clues: unfamiliar words		Language 4.a.	0 1
25.	Dictionary/glossary: multiple-meaning words		Language 4.c.	0 1
26.	Dictionary/glossary: multiple-meaning words		Language 4.c.	0 1
27.	Dictionary/glossary: multiple-meaning words		Language 4.c.	0 1
28.	Word structure: prefixes		Language 4.a.	0 1
29.	Dictionary/glossary: unfamiliar words		Language 4.c.	0 1

- - - E v a l u a t i o n   C h a r t :   G r a d e   6   —   U n i t   4   B e n c h m a r k   T e s t - - -

Reading – Part 2: Vocabulary (continued)				
30.	Context clues: unfamiliar words	Language 4.a.	0	1
31.	Context clues: unfamiliar words	Language 4.a.	0	1
32.	Context clues: multiple-meaning words	Language 4.a.	0	1
Student's Regrouping Multiple-Choice Score/Total Possible Score _____			**/32**	
Reading – Part 3: Writing Conventions				
33.	Subject and object pronouns	Language 1.a.	0	1
34.	Subject and object pronouns	Language 1.a.	0	1
35.	Subject and object pronouns	Language 1.a.	0	1
36.	Pronouns and antecedents	Language 1.d.	0	1
37.	Pronouns and antecedents	Language 1.d.	0	1
38.	Indefinite pronouns	Language 1.	0	1
39.	Possessive pronouns	Language 1.	0	1
40.	Reflexive pronouns	Language 1.b.	0	1
Student's Reading Total Score/Total Possible Score _____			**/44**	

*L = literal   I = inferential   C = critical analysis

Regrouping (Reading — Parts 1–2) percentage score: _____ ÷ 32 = _____ × 100 = _____ %
                                                                  (student's score)   (percentage score)

Reading — Parts 1–3 percentage score: _____ ÷ 44 = _____ × 100 = _____ %
                                                              (student's total score)   (percentage score)

Writing – Part 4	
Writing Score (complete one) _____ /6 _____ /5 _____ /4 _____ /3	**Common Core State Standards**
Notes/Observations:	Writing 3. Writing 4. Writing 10. Language 1. Language 2.

Evaluation Chart: Grade 6 — Unit 5 Benchmark Test

Student Name _____ Date _____

	Reading – Parts 1–3			
Item	**Tested Skill**	**Item Type***	**Common Core State Standard**	**Score** (circle one)
Reading – Part 1: Comprehension				
1.	Sequence	L	Literature 5.	0 1
2.	Literary elements: plot	I	Literature 3.	0 1
3.	Cause and effect	L	Literature 1.	0 1
4.	Literary elements: plot	I	Literature 3.	0 1
5.	Literary elements: theme	C	Literature 2.	0 1
6.	Author's purpose	C	Literature 1.	0 1
7.	Cause and effect	I	Literature 3.	0 1
8.	Literary elements: plot	C	Literature 3.	0 1
9.	Cause and effect	C	Literature 3.	0 1
10.	Literary elements: theme	C	Literature 2.	0 1
11.	Literary elements: characters	C	Literature 3.	0 1
A.	Constructed-response text-to-self connection		Writing 3.	0 1 2
12.	Cause and effect	L	Literature 3.	0 1
13.	Cause and effect	L	Literature 3.	0 1
14.	Cause and effect	L	Literature 3.	0 1
15.	Sequence	C	Literature 1.	0 1
16.	Author's purpose	C	Literature 1.	0 1
17.	Literary elements: setting	I	Literature 5.	0 1
18.	Literary elements: character	I	Literature 3.	0 1
19.	Literary elements: plot	L	Literature 3.	0 1
20.	Literary elements: plot	I	Literature 3.	0 1
21.	Literary elements: theme	C	Literature 2.	0 1
22.	Main idea and details	I	Literature 2.	0 1
B.	Constructed-response text-to-text connection		Writing 2.	0 1 2
Reading – Part 2: Vocabulary				
23.	Context clues: antonyms		Language 4.a.	0 1
24.	Context clues: synonyms		Language 4.a.	0 1
25.	Context clues: homonyms		Language 4.a.	0 1
26.	Context clues: unfamiliar words		Language 4.a.	0 1
27.	Context clues: antonyms		Language 4.a.	0 1
28.	Context clues: unfamiliar words		Language 4.a.	0 1
29.	Context clues: homonyms		Language 4.a.	0 1

- - - - - - Evaluation Chart: Grade 6 — Unit 5 Benchmark Test - - - - - - -

Reading – Part 2: Vocabulary (continued)			
30.	Context clues: homonyms	Language 4.a.	0 1
31.	Context clues: synonyms	Language 4.a.	0 1
32.	Context clues: antonyms	Language 4.a.	0 1
Student's Regrouping Multiple-Choice Score/Total Possible Score _____ /32			
Reading – Part 3: Writing Conventions			
33.	Contractions and negatives	Language 2.	0 1
34.	Contractions and negatives	Language 1.	0 1
35.	Predicate adjectives	Language 1.	0 1
36.	Proper adjectives	Language 2.	0 1
37.	Demonstrative pronouns	Language 1.	0 1
38.	Comparative and superlative adjectives	Language 1.	0 1
39.	Adjective clauses	Language 1.	0 1
40.	Adverb phrases	Language 1.	0 1
Student's Reading Total Score/Total Possible Score _____ /44			

*L = literal   I = inferential   C = critical analysis

Regrouping (Reading — Parts 1–2) percentage score: _____ ÷ 32 = _____ × 100 = _____ %

(student's score)   (percentage score)

Reading — Parts 1–3 percentage score: _____ ÷ 44 = _____ × 100 = _____ %

(student's total score)   (percentage score)

Writing – Part 4	
Writing Score (complete one) _____ /6 _____ /5 _____ /4 _____ /3	**Common Core State Standards**
Notes/Observations:	Writing 1. Writing 4. Writing 10. Language 1. Language 2.

Evaluation Chart: Grade 6 — Unit 6 Benchmark Test

Student Name _____ Date _____

Item	Tested Skill	Item Type*	Common Core State Standard	Score (circle one)
Reading – Parts 1–3				
Reading – Part 1: Comprehension				
1.	Compare and contrast	I	Literature 1.	0 1
2.	Compare and contrast	I	Literature 1.	0 1
3.	Draw conclusions	I	Literature 3.	0 1
4.	Cause and effect	I	Literature 3.	0 1
5.	Main idea and details	I	Literature 2.	0 1
6.	Compare and contrast	L	Literature 1.	0 1
7.	Compare and contrast	I	Literature 5.	0 1
8.	Generalize	C	Literature 1.	0 1
9.	Draw conclusions	I	Literature 1.	0 1
10.	Author's purpose	C	Literature 1.	0 1
11.	Literary elements: theme	C	Literature 2.	0 1
A.	Constructed-response text-to-world connection		Writing 2.	0 1 2
12.	Draw conclusions	C	Informational Text 1.	0 1
13.	Compare and contrast	I	Informational Text 8.	0 1
14.	Compare and contrast	I	Informational Text 8.	0 1
15.	Draw conclusions	I	Informational Text 5.	0 1
16.	Sequence	I	Informational Text 1.	0 1
17.	Compare and contrast	L	Informational Text 8.	0 1
18.	Main idea and details	I	Informational Text 2.	0 1
19.	Fact and opinion	C	Informational Text 8.	0 1
20.	Author's purpose	C	Informational Text 6.	0 1
21.	Main idea and details	I	Informational Text 2.	0 1
22.	Draw conclusions	C	Informational Text 1.	0 1
B.	Constructed-response text-to-text connection		Writing 2.	0 1 2
Reading – Part 2: Vocabulary				
23.	Context clues: multiple-meaning words		Language 4.a.	0 1
24.	Context clues: unfamiliar words		Language 4.a.	0 1
25.	Context clues: multiple-meaning words		Language 4.a.	0 1
26.	Context clues: multiple-meaning words		Language 4.a.	0 1
27.	Context clues: synonyms		Language 4.a.	0 1
28.	Context clues: unfamiliar words		Language 4.a.	0 1
29.	Context clues: unfamiliar words		Language 4.a.	0 1

Reading – Part 2: Vocabulary (continued)			
30.	Context clues: multiple-meaning words	Language 4.a.	0 1
31.	Context clues: synonyms	Language 4.a.	0 1
32.	Context clues: unfamiliar words	Language 4.a.	0 1
Student's Regrouping Multiple-Choice Score/Total Possible Score			_____ /32
Reading – Part 3: Writing Conventions			
33.	Commas	Language 2.a.	0 1
34.	Quotations	Language 2.	0 1
35.	Commas	Language 2.a.	0 1
36.	Conjunctions	Language 2.	0 1
37.	Commas	Language 2.a.	0 1
38.	Commas	Language 2.a.	0 1
39.	Commas	Language 2.a.	0 1
40.	Conjunctions	Language 2.	0 1
Student's Reading Total Score/Total Possible Score			_____ /44

*L = literal   I = inferential   C = critical analysis

Regrouping (Reading — Parts 1–2) percentage score: _____ ÷ 32 = _____ × 100 = _____%

(student's score)   (percentage score)

Reading — Parts 1–3 percentage score: _____ ÷ 44 = _____ × 100 = _____%

(student's total score)   (percentage score)

Writing – Part 4	Common Core State Standards
Writing Score (complete one) _____ /6 _____ /5 _____ /4 _____ /3	
Notes/Observations:	Writing 2. Writing 4. Writing 10. Language 1. Language 2.

Evaluation Chart: Grade 6 — End-of-Year Benchmark Test

Student Name _____ Date _____

Reading – Parts 1–3

Item	Tested Skill	Item Type*	Common Core State Standard	Score (circle one)
Reading – Part 1: Comprehension				
1.	Literary elements: character	I	Literature 1.	0 1
2.	Literary elements: setting	L	Literature 1.	0 1
3.	Literary elements: character	I	Literature 1.	0 1
4.	Literary elements: plot	C	Literature 3.	0 1
5.	Sequence	I	Literature 5.	0 1
6.	Draw conclusions	I	Literature 3.	0 1
7.	Literary elements: character	I	Literature 3.	0 1
8.	Cause and effect	I	Literature 3.	0 1
9.	Draw conclusions	I	Literature 1.	0 1
10.	Literary elements: plot	C	Literature 3.	0 1
11.	Sequence	L	Literature 5.	0 1
12.	Fact and opinion	C	Informational Text 6.	0 1
13.	Author's purpose	C	Informational Text 6.	0 1
14.	Sequence	I	Informational Text 5.	0 1
15.	Generalize	C	Informational Text 8.	0 1
16.	Main idea and details	L	Informational Text 2.	0 1
17.	Cause and effect	L	Informational Text 3.	0 1
18.	Draw conclusions	C	Informational Text 3.	0 1
19.	Main idea and details	C	Informational Text 2.	0 1
20.	Compare and contrast	I	Informational Text 8.	0 1
21.	Draw conclusions	C	Informational Text 3.	0 1
22.	Main idea and details	I	Informational Text 2.	0 1
A.	Constructed-response text-to-text connection		Writing 2.	0 1 2
23.	Draw conclusions	I	Informational Text 2.	0 1
24.	Fact and opinion	C	Informational Text 6.	0 1
25.	Compare and contrast	I	Informational Text 3.	0 1
26.	Main idea and details	I	Informational Text 8.	0 1
27.	Cause and effect	L	Informational Text 1.	0 1
28.	Graphic sources	I	Informational Text 7.	0 1
29.	Author's purpose	C	Informational Text 6.	0 1
30.	Sequence	L	Informational Text 5.	0 1
31.	Author's purpose	C	Informational Text 6.	0 1
32.	Graphic sources	I	Informational Text 7.	0 1
33.	Graphic sources	I	Informational Text 7.	0 1
B.	Constructed-response text-to-text connection		Writing 2.	0 1 2

Reading – Part 2: Vocabulary

34.	Word structure: suffixes	Language 1.	0 1
35.	Dictionary/glossary: unfamiliar words	Language 4.c	0 1
36.	Dictionary/glossary: multiple-meaning words	Language 4.c.	0 1
37.	Context clues: unfamiliar words	Language 4.a.	0 1
38.	Word structure: prefixes	Language 4.a.	0 1
39.	Word structure: prefixes	Language 4.b.	0 1
40.	Word structure: base words	Language 4.b.	0 1
41.	Context clues: homonyms	Language 4.a.	0 1
42.	Context clues: synonyms	Language 5.	0 1
43.	Context clues: synonyms	Language 4.a.	0 1
44.	Context clues: unfamiliar words	Language 4.a.	0 1
45.	Dictionary/glossary: multiple-meaning words	Language 4.c.	0 1
46.	Dictionary/glossary: multiple-meaning words	Language 4.c.	0 1
47.	Word structure: prefixes	Language 4.b.	0 1
48.	Word structure: base words	Language 5.	0 1

Reading – Part 3: Writing Conventions

49.	Sentences	Language 1.	0 1
50.	Compound and complex sentences	Language 1.	0 1
51.	Action and linking verbs	Language 1.	0 1
52.	Subject and object complements	Language 1.	0 1
53.	Irregular plural nouns	Language 2.b.	0 1
54.	Comparative and superlative adjectives	Language 1.	0 1
55.	Subject-verb agreement	Language 1.	0 1
56.	Irregular verbs	Language 1.	0 1
57.	Possessive nouns	Language 2.b.	0 1
58.	Quotation marks	Language 2.	0 1
59.	Proper nouns and adjectives	Language 2.	0 1
60.	Pronouns	Language 1.a.	0 1
Student's Reading Total Score/Total Possible Score		**_____ /64**	

*L = literal   I = inferential   C = critical analysis

Reading — Parts 1–3 percentage score: _____ ÷ 64 = _____ × 100 = _____ %
          (student's total score)   (percentage score)

Writing – Part 4	
Writing Score (complete one) _____ /6 _____ /5 _____ /4 _____ /3	**Common Core State Standards**
Notes/Observations:	Writing 1. Writing 4. Writing 10. Language 1. Language 2.

CLASS RECORD CHART

Grade 6 Unit Benchmark Tests

Teacher Name _____ Class _____

Student Name	Unit 1		Unit 2		Unit 3		Unit 4		Unit 5		Unit 6	
	Pt 1–3	Pt 4	Pt 1–3	Pt 4	Pt 1–3	Pt 4	Pt 1–3	Pt 4	Pt 1–3	Pt 4	Pt 1–3	Pt 4
1.												
2.												
3.												
4.												
5.												
6.												
7.												
8.												
9.												
10.												
11.												
12.												
13.												
14.												
15.												
16.												
17.												
18.												
19.												
20.												
21.												
22.												
23.												
24.												
25.												
26.												
27.												
28.												
29.												
30.												

ANSWER KEYS

Unit 1 Benchmark Test

Reading – Part 1: Comprehension

Selection 1: "Not Defeated Yet!"

1. A
2. H
3. D
4. F
5. D
6. H
7. A
8. J
9. B
10. G
11. D

A. Use the Constructed-Response Scoring Rubric on page T11 to help you assess students' responses. Assign each response a score from 0 to 2.

A possible top response might be:

If the story took place in a farm community, people might not live close enough to work on a garden together, and they might not even need a Victory Garden, because everyone would have the space to grow their own fruits and vegetables.

Selection 2: "The Texas Bat Woman"

12. F
13. B
14. G
15. B
16. H
17. D
18. F
19. D
20. H
21. C
22. G

B. Use the Constructed-Response Scoring Rubric on page T11 to help you assess students' responses. Assign each response a score from 0 to 2.

A possible top response might be:

Marcie Kennedy began to care about the Victory Garden that had been in the lot next to her building. She wanted to start the garden going again, so her grandfather could enjoy it again. Amanda Lollar began to care about bats, after rescuing one that she found in front of her family's furniture store.

Reading – Part 2: Vocabulary

23. C
24. J
25. C
26. F
27. C
28. F
29. D
30. G
31. D
32. J

Reading – Part 3: Writing Conventions

33. B
34. G
35. C
36. H
37. B

38. G

39. C

40. F

Writing – Part 4

Prompt: Students are asked to write a story about a time in their life when they felt the need to help someone. They are to include details about the experience and how it changed them.

Scoring: Use one of the Narrative Writing Scoring Rubrics on pages T12–T13 to help you assess students' compositions. Choose one of the four rubrics, and assign each composition a score based on the 6-point, 5-point, 4-point, or 3-point scale.

Unit 2 Benchmark Test

Reading – Part 1: Comprehension

Selection 1: "The Gullah of the Sea Islands"

1. C

2. G

3. C

4. F

5. A

6. G

7. D

8. G

9. D

10. J

11. D

A. Use the Constructed-Response Scoring Rubric on page T11 to help you assess students' responses. Assign each response a score from 0 to 2.

A possible top response might be:

When bridges were built connecting the Sea Islands to the mainland, many Gullah people sold their land and left. As more people from the outside world came to the Sea Islands, the Gullah ways began to disappear. So, Gullah leaders responded by starting the Gullah Festival. It happens every year, and it celebrates Gullah culture.

Selection 2: "Mariachi Musician in Michigan"

12. J

13. C

14. F

15. A

16. J

17. A

18. G

19. D

20. J

21. C

22. G

B. Use the Constructed-Response Scoring Rubric on page T11 to help you assess students' responses. Assign each response a score from 0 to 2.

A possible top response might be:

Gullah people connect with the past by taking part in the Gullah Festival and continuing their traditional cooking, crafts, language, and storytelling. The narrator in "Mariachi Musician in Michigan" connects with the past by playing mariachi, the music of his elder Mexican relatives. In both cases, these connections are important because they make the people feel proud and help keep their traditional cultures alive.

Reading – Part 2: Vocabulary

23. B
24. H
25. D
26. G
27. A
28. J
29. D
30. H
31. B
32. F

Reading – Part 3: Writing Conventions

33. B
34. F
35. B
36. J
37. D
38. H
39. C
40. G

Writing – Part 4

Prompt: Students are asked to write a report on how they would go about researching and writing a paper on a member of their family who lived at least fifty years ago.

Scoring: Use one of the Expository Writing Scoring Rubrics on pages T16–T17 to help you assess students' compositions. Choose one of the four rubrics, and assign each composition a score based on the 6-point, 5-point, 4-point, or 3-point scale.

Unit 3 Benchmark Test

Reading – Part 1: Comprehension

Selection 1: "The Peach Seed"

1. C
2. F
3. B
4. G
5. C
6. G
7. A
8. G
9. D
10. G
11. D

A. Use the Constructed-Response Scoring Rubric on page T11 to help you assess students' responses. Assign each response a score from 0 to 2.

A possible top response might be:

Before he went to prison, Gerhard thought it was okay to steal. He tried to steal Rosamund's wedding ring, even though he promised to be honest if she would marry him. After being in prison, he decided that honesty was better, since prison was so horrible. The peach seed in his pocket reminded him that "honesty brings great rewards," as the last line of the story states.

Unit 3 Benchmark Test

Selection 2: "Wilma Rudolph"

12. G

13. D

14. H

15. B

16. F

17. A

18. H

19. B

20. F

21. B

22. J

B. Use the Constructed-Response Scoring Rubric on page T11 to help you assess students' responses. Assign each response a score from 0 to 2.

A possible top response might be:

When Gerhard finally met Rosamund's challenge to become an honest man, his reward was to be able to marry her, have a son, and live a happy life. Wilma Rudolph faced the challenges of her many health problems, but she overcame them with hard work and was rewarded with fans' appreciation, medals, and the reputation as "the fastest woman in the world."

Reading – Part 2: Vocabulary

23. D

24. H

25. A

26. J

27. B

28. F

29. A

30. H

31. B

32. J

Reading – Part 3: Writing Conventions

33. B

34. J

35. B

36. H

37. D

38. G

39. A

40. J

Writing – Part 4

Prompt: Students are asked to write an essay that compares and contrasts two things they have done—one easy thing and one difficult thing. Then they describe how they felt about these experiences.

Scoring: Use one of the Expository Writing Scoring Rubrics on pages T16–T17 to help you assess students' compositions. Choose one of the four rubrics, and assign each composition a score based on the 6-point, 5-point, 4-point, or 3-point scale.

Unit 4 Benchmark Test

Reading – Part 1: Comprehension

Selection 1: "Emily Roebling and the Building of the Brooklyn Bridge"

1. D

2. J

3. B

4. H

5. A

6. J

7. C

8. G

9. B

10. J

11. C

A. Use the Constructed-Response Scoring Rubric on page T11 to help you assess students' responses. Assign each response a score from 0 to 2.

A possible top response might be:

The Roebling family showed courage and persistence. John Roebling was the chief engineer, and he was a famous bridge builder. He convinced others that the Brooklyn Bridge was possible. When John died, his son Washington took over. Even when he was sick, he didn't give up. Washington's wife, Emily, showed great courage to do things that other women didn't do. She took over for Washington in supervising the building of the famous bridge.

Selection 2: "Neal Writes a Letter"

12. F

13. B

14. J

15. C

16. H

17. A

18. G

19. A

20. J

21. D

22. F

B. Use the Constructed-Response Scoring Rubric on page T11 to help you assess students' responses. Assign each response a score from 0 to 2.

A possible top response might be:

Neal and Roger used sand and driftwood, whereas the Roeblings used stone and cables. While the Roeblings were building the Brooklyn Bridge, many problems occurred, including a fire. Neal and Roger had to figure out how to build a sand bridge using driftwood as a support. They faced the challenge of bad weather.

Reading – Part 2: Vocabulary

23. D

24. G

25. C

26. F

27. B

28. G

29. D

30. F

31. B

32. J

Reading – Part 3: Writing Conventions

33. D

34. F

35. C

36. F

37. A

38. H

39. C

40. H

Writing – Part 4

Prompt: Students are asked to write a story describing a challenge they faced and what they did to overcome it.

Scoring: Use one of the Narrative Writing Scoring Rubrics on pages T12–T13 to help you assess students' compositions. Choose one of the four rubrics, and assign each composition a score based on the 6-point, 5-point, 4-point, or 3-point scale.

Unit 5 Benchmark Test

Reading – Part 1: Comprehension

Selection 1: "Lexie Lends a Hand"

1. B
2. H
3. A
4. H
5. C
6. G
7. A
8. J
9. D
10. G
11. A

A. Use the Constructed-Response Scoring Rubric on page T11 to help you assess students' responses. Assign each response a score from 0 to 2.

A possible top response might be:

Lexie started off complaining about being too young to do anything she wanted to do. Her brothers told her to quit whining and to start thinking about what she could do for herself. She changed her attitude and got busy and was happy in the end.

Selection 2: "Rice from a Cat's Fur: A Retelling of a Korean Folk Tale"

12. H
13. B
14. H
15. B
16. J
17. C
18. F
19. C
20. H
21. B
22. J

B. Use the Constructed-Response Scoring Rubric on page T11 to help you assess students' responses. Assign each response a score from 0 to 2.

A possible top response might be:

Lexie solved her problem by listening to her brothers' advice to use her own skills and resources. The daughters solved the problem of having no food by rubbing a magical cat that yielded rice.

Reading – Part 2: Vocabulary

23. A
24. F
25. C
26. J
27. A
28. G
29. D
30. G
31. B
32. J

Reading – Part 3: Writing Conventions

33. A

34. G

35. C

36. H

37. D

38. G

39. B

40. G

Writing – Part 4

Prompt: Students are asked to think about a cause or topic they strongly believe in and write a paper to convince others to agree with their point of view.

Scoring: Use one of the Persuasive Writing Scoring Rubrics on pages T18–T19 to help you assess students' compositions. Choose one of the four rubrics, and assign each composition a score based on the 6-point, 5-point, 4-point, or 3-point scale.

Unit 6 Benchmark Test

Reading – Part 1: Comprehension

Selection 1: "A Letter from America"

1. A

2. H

3. B

4. J

5. B

6. F

7. C

8. J

9. D

10. G

11. C

A. Use the Constructed-Response Scoring Rubric on page T11 to help you assess students' responses. Assign each response a score from 0 to 2.

A possible top response might be:

The city I live in is not as big as Peter's city, yet it is also filled with people from different cultures who speak different languages. People from all over the world attend our large university. People work hard here as they do in Peter's city, and, in most cases, husbands and wives have jobs. Boys and girls go to school, and most graduate from high school and go to college. There is some poverty, and we are lucky to have organizations that help the poor by giving them food and shelter.

Selection 2: "Native Americans: Algonquin and Iroquois"

12. J

13. A

14. F

15. B

16. H

17. D

18. G

19. A

20. G

21. B

22. J

B. Use the Constructed-Response Scoring Rubric on page T11 to help you assess students' responses. Assign each response a score from 0 to 2.

A possible top response might be:

Both "A Letter from America" and "Algonquin and Iroquois" are about societies of people in America, except that "Letter" is fiction, and "Algonquin and Iroquois" is nonfiction. "Letter" is written from the point of view of a newcomer to the land, while the other describes the original inhabitants of the land. In both texts people work very hard to make a living and take care of their families. The Algonquin and Iroquois lived off the land, while the writer of "Letter" worked in the city.

Reading – Part 2: Vocabulary

23. A
24. G
25. C
26. J
27. D
28. G
29. A
30. J
31. B
32. J

Reading – Part 3: Writing Conventions

33. B
34. F
35. C
36. F
37. B
38. H
39. C
40. J

Writing – Part 4

Prompt: Students are asked to write an essay comparing two people they know who live very different kinds of lives.

Scoring: Use one of the Descriptive Writing Scoring Rubrics on pages T14–T15 to help you assess students' compositions. Choose one of the four rubrics, and assign each composition a score based on the 6-point, 5-point, 4-point, or 3-point scale.

End-of-Year Benchmark Test

Reading – Part 1: Comprehension

Selection 1: "Kayla's Problem"

1. B
2. F
3. B
4. H
5. C
6. J
7. C
8. G
9. D
10. J
11. A

Selection 2: "The Man Behind the Prize"

12. F
13. C
14. H
15. C
16. F
17. B
18. F
19. B
20. J
21. D
22. G

A. Use the Constructed-Response Scoring Rubric on page T11 to help you assess students' responses. Assign each response a score from 0 to 2.

A possible top response might be:

Kayla and Nobel both valued making a contribution to humanity. Kayla showed this by wanting to donate her hair, and Nobel showed it by setting up prizes for those who had made such contributions.

Selection 3: "A Different Kind of Bank"

23. B

24. F

25. D

26. G

27. D

28. H

29. A

30. G

31. C

32. J

33. D

B. Use the Constructed-Response Scoring Rubric on page T11 to help you assess students' responses. Assign each response a score from 0 to 2.

A possible top response might be:

The authors had the same purpose: to inform the reader. In "The Man Behind the Prize," the author organized the information in chronological order, based on when events happened in Nobel's life. In "A Different Kind of Bank," the author started with specific examples of poor people and then moved to the general idea of helping them through microcredit.

Reading – Part 2: Vocabulary

34. H

35. C

36. F

37. B

38. F

39. C

40. H

41. D

42. G

43. D

44. F

45. B

46. J

47. A

48. H

Reading – Part 3: Writing Conventions

49. B

50. H

51. D

52. G

53. A

54. F

55. C

56. H

57. B

58. J

59. D

60. G

Writing – Part 4

Prompt: Students are asked to write an essay about an idea or invention they consider important. The essay should convince readers of the importance of the idea or invention by giving reasons in support of the viewpoint.

Scoring: Use one of the Persuasive Writing Scoring Rubrics on pages T18–T19 to help you assess students' compositions. Choose one of the four rubrics, and assign each composition a score based on the 6-point, 5-point, 4-point, or 3-point scale.

ANSWER SHEET

Unit Benchmark Tests

Student Name _____ Unit _____

Teacher Name _____ Date _____

Important Directions for Marking Answers

- Use black lead pencil (No. 2).
- Make heavy dark marks that fill the circle completely.
- Erase completely any answers you wish to change.
- If you erase a grid circle, do not redraw it.
- Do not make any stray marks on this answer sheet.

CORRECT MARK

Ⓐ ● Ⓒ Ⓓ

INCORRECT MARKS

Reading – Part 1: Comprehension

1. Ⓐ Ⓑ Ⓒ Ⓓ   6. Ⓕ Ⓖ Ⓗ Ⓙ   11. Ⓐ Ⓑ Ⓒ Ⓓ   16. Ⓕ Ⓖ Ⓗ Ⓙ   21. Ⓐ Ⓑ Ⓒ Ⓓ
2. Ⓕ Ⓖ Ⓗ Ⓙ   7. Ⓐ Ⓑ Ⓒ Ⓓ   12. Ⓕ Ⓖ Ⓗ Ⓙ   17. Ⓐ Ⓑ Ⓒ Ⓓ   22. Ⓕ Ⓖ Ⓗ Ⓙ
3. Ⓐ Ⓑ Ⓒ Ⓓ   8. Ⓕ Ⓖ Ⓗ Ⓙ   13. Ⓐ Ⓑ Ⓒ Ⓓ   18. Ⓕ Ⓖ Ⓗ Ⓙ
4. Ⓕ Ⓖ Ⓗ Ⓙ   9. Ⓐ Ⓑ Ⓒ Ⓓ   14. Ⓕ Ⓖ Ⓗ Ⓙ   19. Ⓐ Ⓑ Ⓒ Ⓓ
5. Ⓐ Ⓑ Ⓒ Ⓓ   10. Ⓕ Ⓖ Ⓗ Ⓙ   15. Ⓐ Ⓑ Ⓒ Ⓓ   20. Ⓕ Ⓖ Ⓗ Ⓙ

Reading – Part 2: Vocabulary

23. Ⓐ Ⓑ Ⓒ Ⓓ   25. Ⓐ Ⓑ Ⓒ Ⓓ   27. Ⓐ Ⓑ Ⓒ Ⓓ   29. Ⓐ Ⓑ Ⓒ Ⓓ   31. Ⓐ Ⓑ Ⓒ Ⓓ
24. Ⓕ Ⓖ Ⓗ Ⓙ   26. Ⓕ Ⓖ Ⓗ Ⓙ   28. Ⓕ Ⓖ Ⓗ Ⓙ   30. Ⓕ Ⓖ Ⓗ Ⓙ   32. Ⓕ Ⓖ Ⓗ Ⓙ

Reading – Part 3: Writing Conventions

33. Ⓐ Ⓑ Ⓒ Ⓓ   35. Ⓐ Ⓑ Ⓒ Ⓓ   37. Ⓐ Ⓑ Ⓒ Ⓓ   39. Ⓐ Ⓑ Ⓒ Ⓓ
34. Ⓕ Ⓖ Ⓗ Ⓙ   36. Ⓕ Ⓖ Ⓗ Ⓙ   38. Ⓕ Ⓖ Ⓗ Ⓙ   40. Ⓕ Ⓖ Ⓗ Ⓙ

ANSWER SHEET

End-of-Year Benchmark Test

Student Name _____ Date _____

Teacher Name _____

Important Directions for Marking Answers

- Use black lead pencil (No. 2).
- Make heavy dark marks that fill the circle completely.
- Erase completely any answers you wish to change.
- If you erase a grid circle, do not redraw it.
- Do not make any stray marks on this answer sheet.

CORRECT MARK

Ⓐ ● Ⓒ Ⓓ

INCORRECT MARKS

Reading – Part 1: Comprehension

1. Ⓐ Ⓑ Ⓒ Ⓓ   8. Ⓕ Ⓖ Ⓗ Ⓙ   15. Ⓐ Ⓑ Ⓒ Ⓓ   22. Ⓕ Ⓖ Ⓗ Ⓙ   29. Ⓐ Ⓑ Ⓒ Ⓓ

2. Ⓕ Ⓖ Ⓗ Ⓙ   9. Ⓐ Ⓑ Ⓒ Ⓓ   16. Ⓕ Ⓖ Ⓗ Ⓙ   23. Ⓐ Ⓑ Ⓒ Ⓓ   30. Ⓕ Ⓖ Ⓗ Ⓙ

3. Ⓐ Ⓑ Ⓒ Ⓓ   10. Ⓕ Ⓖ Ⓗ Ⓙ   17. Ⓐ Ⓑ Ⓒ Ⓓ   24. Ⓕ Ⓖ Ⓗ Ⓙ   31. Ⓐ Ⓑ Ⓒ Ⓓ

4. Ⓕ Ⓖ Ⓗ Ⓙ   11. Ⓐ Ⓑ Ⓒ Ⓓ   18. Ⓕ Ⓖ Ⓗ Ⓙ   25. Ⓐ Ⓑ Ⓒ Ⓓ   32. Ⓕ Ⓖ Ⓗ Ⓙ

5. Ⓐ Ⓑ Ⓒ Ⓓ   12. Ⓕ Ⓖ Ⓗ Ⓙ   19. Ⓐ Ⓑ Ⓒ Ⓓ   26. Ⓕ Ⓖ Ⓗ Ⓙ   33. Ⓐ Ⓑ Ⓒ Ⓓ

6. Ⓕ Ⓖ Ⓗ Ⓙ   13. Ⓐ Ⓑ Ⓒ Ⓓ   20. Ⓕ Ⓖ Ⓗ Ⓙ   27. Ⓐ Ⓑ Ⓒ Ⓓ

7. Ⓐ Ⓑ Ⓒ Ⓓ   14. Ⓕ Ⓖ Ⓗ Ⓙ   21. Ⓐ Ⓑ Ⓒ Ⓓ   28. Ⓕ Ⓖ Ⓗ Ⓙ

Reading – Part 2: Vocabulary

34. Ⓕ Ⓖ Ⓗ Ⓙ   37. Ⓐ Ⓑ Ⓒ Ⓓ   40. Ⓕ Ⓖ Ⓗ Ⓙ   43. Ⓐ Ⓑ Ⓒ Ⓓ   46. Ⓕ Ⓖ Ⓗ Ⓙ

35. Ⓐ Ⓑ Ⓒ Ⓓ   38. Ⓕ Ⓖ Ⓗ Ⓙ   41. Ⓐ Ⓑ Ⓒ Ⓓ   44. Ⓕ Ⓖ Ⓗ Ⓙ   47. Ⓐ Ⓑ Ⓒ Ⓓ

36. Ⓕ Ⓖ Ⓗ Ⓙ   39. Ⓐ Ⓑ Ⓒ Ⓓ   42. Ⓕ Ⓖ Ⓗ Ⓙ   45. Ⓐ Ⓑ Ⓒ Ⓓ   48. Ⓕ Ⓖ Ⓗ Ⓙ

Reading – Part 3: Writing Conventions

49. Ⓐ Ⓑ Ⓒ Ⓓ   52. Ⓕ Ⓖ Ⓗ Ⓙ   55. Ⓐ Ⓑ Ⓒ Ⓓ   58. Ⓕ Ⓖ Ⓗ Ⓙ

50. Ⓕ Ⓖ Ⓗ Ⓙ   53. Ⓐ Ⓑ Ⓒ Ⓓ   56. Ⓕ Ⓖ Ⓗ Ⓙ   59. Ⓐ Ⓑ Ⓒ Ⓓ

51. Ⓐ Ⓑ Ⓒ Ⓓ   54. Ⓕ Ⓖ Ⓗ Ⓙ   57. Ⓐ Ⓑ Ⓒ Ⓓ   60. Ⓕ Ⓖ Ⓗ Ⓙ

OPTIONAL — FLUENCY CHECKS OR RUNNING RECORDS

How to Administer and Score a Fluency Test

A fluency test measures a student's reading rate, or the number of words read correctly per minute (wcpm), on grade-level text the student has not seen before. Give the student a copy of the Student Copy of the passage for the test and make a copy of the Teacher Copy for yourself, noting the formula for calculation at the bottom of the page. (The Teacher Copy has a scale of running numbers to make it easier for you to know how many words the student read during the fluency check, while the passage on the Student Copy does not have the numbers.) Make sure you have put the student's name and the test date at the top of your copy of the passage. Have a watch or clock with a second hand available for timing the reading.

Have the student read the text aloud. Do not have the student read the title as part of the fluency reading; it is not included in the running word count. (You may want to tape-record the student's reading for later evaluation.) Stop the student at exactly one minute and note precisely where the student stopped.

As the student reads orally, on your copy of the text, mark any miscues or errors the student makes during the reading (see the chart on page T61). Count the total number of words the student read in one minute. Subtract any words the student read incorrectly. Record the words correct per minute (wcpm) score on the test.

The formula is: Total # of words read – # of errors = words correct per minute (wcpm).

How to Identify Reading Miscues/Errors

Using the passage on page T61, the chart below shows the kinds of miscues and errors to look for as a student reads aloud and the notations to use to mark them.

Reading Miscue	Notations
Omission The student omits words or word parts.	Anjelo (had) visited his cousin in Connecticut the summer before.
Substitution The student substitutes words or parts of words for the words in the text.	As they approached Sells, Michael could see ~~the~~ *a* beautiful green dome on the Pima County Courthouse.
Insertion The student inserts words or parts of words that are not in the text.	Sells wasn't as big or as hot as Michael *had* ∧ expected.
Mispronunciation/Misreading The student pronounces or reads a word incorrectly.	Anjelo knew what Michael ~~expected~~ *accepted* when he came to Arizona.
Hesitation The student hesitates over a word and the teacher provides the word.	So on the ride from the Tuscon airport toward Sells, the capital of the Tohono <u>O'odham</u> Nation near the Mexican border, Michael gaped at the huge saguaro cacti they passed.
Self-correction The student reads a word incorrectly but then corrects the error.	"It's not the biggest Indian *sc* reservation in Arizona."

Notes

- If the student hesitates over a word, wait several seconds before telling the student what the word is.

- If a student makes the same error more than once, count it as only one error.

- Self-correction is not counted as an actual error. However, writing "SC" over the word or words will help you identify words that give the student some difficulty.

Sample Fluency Test

Here is the passage marked as shown on the chart on the previous page. As the student reads the passage aloud to you, mark miscues and errors. Have the student read for exactly one minute, and then mark the last word the student reads.

Student Name *Susan*   Date *9/7/2011*

Anjelo's Nation   (122)

    accepted
Anjelo knew what Michael expected when he came to Arizona. Anjelo (had)   12

visited his cousin in Connecticut the summer before, and Michael kept insisting that   25

Arizona was all a flat, dry desert. So on the ride from the Tucson airport toward   41

                H
Sells, the capital of the Tohono O'odham Nation near the Mexican border, Michael   54

gaped at the huge saguaro cacti they passed.   62

    "Nation," Michael had mumbled the first time he heard the name. "It must really   76

be a small one."   80

                 (sc)
    "It's not the biggest Indian reservation in Arizona," Anjelo agreed, noting that it   93

was, however, about the size of Connecticut.   100

                       a
    As they approached Sells, Michael could see the beautiful green dome on the   113

                                      had
Pima County courthouse. Sells wasn't as big or as hot as Michael ^expected. Anjelo | 127

explained that they were more than two thousand feet above sea level and that it   142

seldom got hotter than eighty degrees there in the summer. Still, Michael couldn't   155

resist suggesting that they stop and buy some bottled water just in case they ran out.   171

127−5=122

Interpreting the Results

According to published norms for oral reading fluency, students at the end of Grade 6 should be reading fluently at 150 words correct per minute in text that is on grade level. This chart gives recommended progress toward that goal.

End of Unit/Grade		Reading Rate (wcpm)
Grade 6	Unit 1	115 to 120
Grade 6	Unit 2	120 to 126
Grade 6	Unit 3	125 to 132
Grade 6	Unit 4	130 to 138
Grade 6	Unit 5	135 to 144
Grade 6	Unit 6	140 to 150
End-of-Year Goal		150

If a student's reading rate is lower than the suggested progress toward the standard for his or her grade level, your notes on the student's miscues may help you determine why the rate is low. Does the student make errors that indicate his or her decoding skills are poor? If so, further instruction in phonics may be needed. Do the errors reflect a lack of comprehension or limited vocabulary? In that case, instruction in comprehension strategies and exposure to more vocabulary words may help. A lack of fluency may indicate a lack of exposure to models of fluent oral reading. It may also mean that the student isn't reading enough material at his or her reading level.

How to Take a Running Record

A Running Record is an assessment of oral reading accuracy and oral reading fluency. A student's reading accuracy is based on the number of words read correctly. This measure is determined by an analysis of the errors a student makes—a miscue analysis. Reading fluency is based on reading rate (the number of words read per minute) and the degree to which the student reads with a "natural flow."

A Running Record may be taken using any reading passage at any time. However, the most valid and reliable assessment fulfills these requirements: (1) the text is appropriate to the student's reading level and interest, and (2) the text is unfamiliar to the student. The passages in this section are well suited for use as either a Fluency Test or with a Running Record because they fit these requirements. For additional oral reading accuracy and fluency checks that involve a Running Record, you may choose other passages from grade-level appropriate texts.

The Running Record may be used to verify instructional decisions suggested by other assessments, such as a Placement or Benchmark Test. It may also be used to identify a student's particular strengths and weaknesses in reading and language development. In addition, the Running Record may be administered periodically throughout the year as a means of monitoring student progress.

Measuring oral reading accuracy and oral reading fluency may be accomplished in a single reading, but two different operations are required. The guidelines on pages T64 and T65 explain how to determine each measurement.

How to Measure Oral Reading Accuracy

1. Choose an appropriate grade-level text of about 100 to 200 words, or use those passages that have been provided for use as a Fluency Test.

2. Make copies of the text—one of the Student Copy for the student and one of the Teacher Copy for you. If the text appears in a book, you may have the student read the text from the book.

3. Give the text to the student and have the student read the text aloud. (You may want to tape-record the student's reading for later evaluation. This approach can be especially helpful if you are timing the student's reading or conducting other assessments at the same time.)

4. Your hand should always be "running" on your copy of the text. Put a checkmark above every word the student reads correctly. Mark any miscues or errors the student makes during the reading (see the explanation of reading miscues/errors for Fluency Tests beginning on page T60).

5. Count the total number of errors the student makes and find the percentage score for the number of errors. If you are using a fluency/running record passage from this book, the total word count is indicated for each passage, and a formula for determining a percentage score is provided.

6. If you are using a text from a different source, use this formula to get a percentage score:

$$\frac{\text{Total \# of words minus \# of errors}}{\text{Total \# of words}} \times 100 = \text{percentage score}$$

Example: Suppose a student reads a text of 110 words and makes 6 errors.

$$\frac{110 - 6 = 104 \text{ words}}{110} = 0.945 \qquad 0.945 \times 100 = 94.5\% \text{ (round to 95\%)}$$

The percentage score indicates the student's oral reading accuracy (percentage of words in the passage read correctly).

How to Measure Reading Rate

Reading rate is generally defined as number of words per minute (wpm). To determine the reading rate, follow steps 1–3 as described on page T64. Note the exact time when the student begins reading and the time when he or she finishes.

To calculate the number of words per minute, use the formula below:

$$\frac{\text{Total \# of words read}}{\text{\# of seconds}} \times 60 = \text{words per minute}$$

Example: Suppose a student reads a passage of 120 words in 90 seconds.

$$\frac{120}{90} = 1.33 \text{ (round to the nearest hundredth)}$$

$$1.33 \times 60 = 79.8 \text{ words per minute (round to 80 wpm)}$$

Interpreting the Results

For oral reading accuracy, use the following criteria:

- A student who reads 98%–100% of the words correctly is reading at an independent level and may need more challenging texts.

- A student who reads 91%–97% of the words correctly is reading at an instructional level and will likely benefit from guided on-level instruction in the regular program.

- A student who reads with an accuracy of 90% or less is reading at a frustration level and may benefit most from targeted instruction with lower-level texts or strategic intervention.

For any student whose Running Record results are not clearly definitive, we recommend administering additional individual assessments, such as classroom observations and anecdotal records. For more information about other assessments, refer to the *Assessment Handbook.*

On the following pages you will find passages that may be used for either fluency or running record tests. Both a Teacher Copy and a Student Copy have been provided.

Student Name _____ Date _____

General Colin L. Powell

Colin Luther Powell was born in New York City on April 5, 1937. His parents	15
had come to this country from Jamaica. He was raised in South Bronx, New York	30
City. He graduated from high school and then went to City College of New York	45
(CCNY). At CCNY, he was part of the Reserve Officers Training Corps (ROTC)	58
program. When he finished school at CCNY in 1958, he became a second lieutenant	72
in the Army. He went on to attend George Washington University, where he studied	86
business.	87
Powell was a career soldier for thirty-five years. During those years he held	100
several command positions, and he was promoted to four-star general in April of	113
1989. Then, in August of that same year, he was named chairman of the Joint Chiefs	129
of Staff, the person who commands all the U.S. Armed Forces. He was the first	144
African American to hold this important post. During his time in this job, there were	159
twenty-eight difficult military situations, including Operation Desert Storm in 1991.	169
After a long career and many honors, Powell retired in 1993.	180
Then, in 2001, President George W. Bush nominated General Powell as U.S.	192
Secretary of State. When the choice was approved, General Powell became the	204
first African American to hold that post. Some of his duties were to serve as the	220
President's principal adviser on U.S. foreign policy and to negotiate all treaties with	233
foreign governments. General Powell resigned in November 2004.	241

Fluency Test

[ ] – [ ] = [ ] (wcpm)

Running Record

Oral Reading Accuracy:

$$\frac{[\ ] - [\ ]}{[\ ]} \times 100 = [\ \ \%]$$

Reading Rate:

$$\frac{[\ ]}{[\ ]} \times 60 = [\ ] \text{(wpm)}$$

General Colin L. Powell

Colin Luther Powell was born in New York City on April 5, 1937. His parents had come to this country from Jamaica. He was raised in South Bronx, New York City. He graduated from high school and then went to City College of New York (CCNY). At CCNY, he was part of the Reserve Officers Training Corps (ROTC) program. When he finished school at CCNY in 1958, he became a second lieutenant in the Army. He went on to attend George Washington University, where he studied business.

Powell was a career soldier for thirty-five years. During those years he held several command positions, and he was promoted to four-star general in April of 1989. Then, in August of that same year, he was named chairman of the Joint Chiefs of Staff, the person who commands all the U.S. Armed Forces. He was the first African American to hold this important post. During his time in this job, there were twenty-eight difficult military situations, including Operation Desert Storm in 1991. After a long career and many honors, Powell retired in 1993.

Then, in 2001, President George W. Bush nominated General Powell as U.S. Secretary of State. When the choice was approved, General Powell became the first African American to hold that post. Some of his duties were to serve as the President's principal adviser on U.S. foreign policy and to negotiate all treaties with foreign governments. General Powell resigned in November 2004.

Student Name _____ Date _____

Harriet Tubman

Araminta Ross was born into slavery in 1820 in Maryland. She was one of	14
eleven children born to Harriet and Benjamin Ross. She was raised under harsh	27
conditions and subjected to whippings as a small child. At the age of twenty-five,	41
Ross married a free African American named John Tubman and changed her name	54
to Harriet. Five years later, fearing that she and others on the plantation were going	69
to be sold, she decided to run away. Her husband refused to go, so she fled with her	87
two brothers. Although her brothers became frightened and turned back, she pressed	99
on. She faithfully followed the North Star, guiding her northward to her freedom,	112
until she reached Philadelphia. There she found work as a domestic servant and	125
saved money so she could return to help others escape.	135
After Tubman escaped slavery, she returned to Maryland not only to rescue her	148
family, which included her seventy-year-old parents, but also to help other enslaved	160
people. Within ten years, she helped more than three hundred enslaved people reach	173
freedom. She led them to the northern free states along the Underground Railroad,	186
a secret network of safe houses where enslaved people who ran away could stay on	201
their journey north to freedom. Whenever Tubman led a group of enslaved people	214
to freedom, she placed herself in great danger. If an enslaved person changed his or	229
her mind, Tubman would pull out a gun and say, "You'll be free or die!" She knew	246
that if anyone turned back, she and the others would be in grave danger.	260

Fluency Test

☐ − ☐ = ☐ (wcpm)

_____

Running Record

Oral Reading Accuracy: Reading Rate:

$$\frac{\boxed{} - \boxed{}}{\boxed{}} \times 100 = \boxed{} \% \qquad \frac{\boxed{}}{\boxed{}} \times 60 = \boxed{} \text{ (wpm)}$$

Harriet Tubman

Araminta Ross was born into slavery in 1820 in Maryland. She was one of eleven children born to Harriet and Benjamin Ross. She was raised under harsh conditions and subjected to whippings as a small child. At the age of twenty-five, Ross married a free African American named John Tubman and changed her name to Harriet. Five years later, fearing that she and others on the plantation were going to be sold, she decided to run away. Her husband refused to go, so she fled with her two brothers. Although her brothers became frightened and turned back, she pressed on. She faithfully followed the North Star, guiding her northward to her freedom, until she reached Philadelphia. There she found work as a domestic servant and saved money so she could return to help others escape.

After Tubman escaped slavery, she returned to Maryland not only to rescue her family, which included her seventy-year-old parents, but also to help other enslaved people. Within ten years, she helped more than three hundred enslaved people reach freedom. She led them to the northern free states along the Underground Railroad, a secret network of safe houses where enslaved people who ran away could stay on their journey north to freedom. Whenever Tubman led a group of enslaved people to freedom, she placed herself in great danger. If an enslaved person changed his or her mind, Tubman would pull out a gun and say, "You'll be free or die!" She knew that if anyone turned back, she and the others would be in grave danger.

Student Name _____ Date _____

The Stray

A powerful wind finally blew away the dark, threatening clouds that had been	13
hovering for three days over the entire town. Rachel had grown bored waiting for	27
the torrential rains to let up and was eager for some sort of adventure in the balmy	44
sun. She asked if she could go to Corina's house around the corner. Her mother	59
agreed, but only on the condition that Rachel would take the trash out. Anxious to	74
leave, Rachel didn't hesitate as she maneuvered the heavy, foul, smelly bag outside	87
to the back fence where the trash can was.	96
As she made her way toward the gritty trash can, Rachel concentrated on	109
avoiding stepping in any mud puddles. Near the fence, something stirred and caught	122
her attention. Rachel stopped dead in her tracks, and whatever it was let out a	137
dreadful, mournful cry. Rachel leaned over gradually and was relieved to see it was	151
a drenched, scared puppy. Rachel reached for the furry, tan bundle, but it growled as	166
it moved away.	169
Then Rachel had a thought and hurried inside to the refrigerator and found the	183
leftover meatloaf on the top shelf. Next, trying hard not to alert her mother, she	198
quietly pulled a tattered blanket from under her bed. With cold meatloaf in one hand	213
and a warm blanket in the other, she tiptoed outside. As she stood there looking at	229
the pathetic creature basking in the warm sunlight, Rachel could think of only two	243
other things she needed to take care of—finding a perfect name for the puppy and	259
determining how to break the news to her mother.	268

Fluency Test

[   ] − [   ] = [   ] (wcpm)

Running Record

Oral Reading Accuracy:

$$\frac{[\quad] - [\quad]}{[\quad]} \times 100 = \boxed{\quad \%}$$

Reading Rate:

$$\frac{[\quad]}{[\quad]} \times 60 = \boxed{\quad} \text{(wpm)}$$

The Stray

A powerful wind finally blew away the dark, threatening clouds that had been hovering for three days over the entire town. Rachel had grown bored waiting for the torrential rains to let up and was eager for some sort of adventure in the balmy sun. She asked if she could go to Corina's house around the corner. Her mother agreed, but only on the condition that Rachel would take the trash out. Anxious to leave, Rachel didn't hesitate as she maneuvered the heavy, foul, smelly bag outside to the back fence where the trash can was.

As she made her way toward the gritty trash can, Rachel concentrated on avoiding stepping in any mud puddles. Near the fence, something stirred and caught her attention. Rachel stopped dead in her tracks, and whatever it was let out a dreadful, mournful cry. Rachel leaned over gradually and was relieved to see it was a drenched, scared puppy. Rachel reached for the furry, tan bundle, but it growled as it moved away.

Then Rachel had a thought and hurried inside to the refrigerator and found the leftover meatloaf on the top shelf. Next, trying hard not to alert her mother, she quietly pulled a tattered blanket from under her bed. With cold meatloaf in one hand and a warm blanket in the other, she tiptoed outside. As she stood there looking at the pathetic creature basking in the warm sunlight, Rachel could think of only two other things she needed to take care of—finding a perfect name for the puppy and determining how to break the news to her mother.

Student Name _____ Date _____

Mount Rushmore

South Dakota is home to the Mount Rushmore National Memorial, a massive	12
sculpture featuring the heads of United States Presidents George Washington,	22
Thomas Jefferson, Abraham Lincoln, and Theodore Roosevelt. The sculpture is	32
carved into the rim of Mount Rushmore and is five hundred feet above the valley	47
floor. Each face is sixty feet tall.	54
The Presidents portrayed were selected on the basis of what each symbolized	66
and for their great skills and leadership. These Presidents laid a foundation for the	80
United States of America as solid as the rock from which their figures are carved.	95
The first President to be carved was George Washington, who represents the	107
struggle and vision for independence. Next to be carved was Thomas Jefferson, who	120
always had dreams of a greater, more perfect nation, as shown first in the words of	136
the Declaration of Independence and later in the expansion of the nation through the	150
Louisiana Purchase. The third President to be carved was Abraham Lincoln, who	162
believed that all men are free and equal. The final President chosen to represent the	177
country on the face of the granite bluff was Theodore Roosevelt, who envisioned a	191
great nation and was a leader on the world stage during the time when the nation	207
changed from a rural republic to a world power. The four Presidents carved in stone	222
represent all Americans in their courage, dreams, freedom, and greatness.	232
The carving of Mount Rushmore began in August of 1927 and took fourteen years	246
to complete. Only about six and a half years were spent actually carving the faces;	261
delays due to weather and the lack of funding accounted for the rest of the time.	277

Fluency Test

☐ – ☐ = ☐ (wcpm)

Running Record

Oral Reading Accuracy:

$$\frac{☐ - ☐}{☐} \times 100 = \boxed{\quad}\ \%$$

Reading Rate:

$$\frac{☐}{☐} \times 60 = \boxed{\quad}\ \text{(wpm)}$$

Mount Rushmore

South Dakota is home to the Mount Rushmore National Memorial, a massive sculpture featuring the heads of United States Presidents George Washington, Thomas Jefferson, Abraham Lincoln, and Theodore Roosevelt. The sculpture is carved into the rim of Mount Rushmore and is five hundred feet above the valley floor. Each face is sixty feet tall.

The Presidents portrayed were selected on the basis of what each symbolized and for their great skills and leadership. These Presidents laid a foundation for the United States of America as solid as the rock from which their figures are carved. The first President to be carved was George Washington, who represents the struggle and vision for independence. Next to be carved was Thomas Jefferson, who always had dreams of a greater, more perfect nation, as shown first in the words of the Declaration of Independence and later in the expansion of the nation through the Louisiana Purchase. The third President to be carved was Abraham Lincoln, who believed that all men are free and equal. The final President chosen to represent the country on the face of the granite bluff was Theodore Roosevelt, who envisioned a great nation and was a leader on the world stage during the time when the nation changed from a rural republic to a world power. The four Presidents carved in stone represent all Americans in their courage, dreams, freedom, and greatness.

The carving of Mount Rushmore began in August of 1927 and took fourteen years to complete. Only about six and a half years were spent actually carving the faces; delays due to weather and the lack of funding accounted for the rest of the time.

Student Name _____ Date _____

Martin

Aromas of spring filled the noontime air as Martin toiled on his family's farm,	14
herding the woolly sheep deep into the hills to the perfect succulent patch for them to	30
graze. As the sheep greedily chomped their way across the fields, Martin, sitting against	44
the old mesquite tree, read aged newspapers his father had collected throughout the	57
years. After the sheep had satisfied their hunger, Martin led them to the thirst-quenching	71
waters of the brook that had carved its own path in the valley below.	85
Martin's parents were humble, hardworking, and worn. His father, up before	96
the crack of dawn, cultivated the rows of beans, maize, and sugarcane that	109
flourished next to the small creek. In the late afternoon, in the cool shade of the	125
house's shadow, he chopped wood for the next day. Awake long before the stars	139
disappeared, Martin's mother, her shiny brunette braid neatly coiled on top of her	152
head, dutifully prepared the first meal before the sun peeked over the horizon.	165
Martha and Rosa, Martin's two younger sisters, meant the world to him.	177
Returning from the hills after the sun had nearly finished its journey across the sky,	192
exhausted by the pounding heat, Martin would meet them by the weather-beaten	204
fence, never forgetting to pluck the most fragrant flowers from the hillside for his	218
sisters and mother to enjoy.	223
That year in the fall, Martin stood at the threshold of Knowledge, aching for the	238
hills of his youth, filled with memories of his family, unprepared for the momentous	252
challenges ahead of him. Still, this was the opportunity of a lifetime and so, with a	268
heavy heart and life-sized dreams, he walked through the old arched doorway and	281
never looked back.	284

Fluency Test

☐ – ☐ = ☐ (wcpm)

Running Record

Oral Reading Accuracy:

$$\frac{\boxed{} - \boxed{}}{\boxed{}} \times 100 = \boxed{}\ \%$$

Reading Rate:

$$\frac{\boxed{}}{\boxed{}} \times 60 = \boxed{}\ (wpm)$$

Martin

Aromas of spring filled the noontime air as Martin toiled on his family's farm, herding the woolly sheep deep into the hills to the perfect succulent patch for them to graze. As the sheep greedily chomped their way across the fields, Martin, sitting against the old mesquite tree, read aged newspapers his father had collected throughout the years. After the sheep had satisfied their hunger, Martin led them to the thirst-quenching waters of the brook that had carved its own path in the valley below.

Martin's parents were humble, hardworking, and worn. His father, up before the crack of dawn, cultivated the rows of beans, maize, and sugarcane that flourished next to the small creek. In the late afternoon, in the cool shade of the house's shadow, he chopped wood for the next day. Awake long before the stars disappeared, Martin's mother, her shiny brunette braid neatly coiled on top of her head, dutifully prepared the first meal before the sun peeked over the horizon.

Martha and Rosa, Martin's two younger sisters, meant the world to him. Returning from the hills after the sun had nearly finished its journey across the sky, exhausted by the pounding heat, Martin would meet them by the weather-beaten fence, never forgetting to pluck the most fragrant flowers from the hillside for his sisters and mother to enjoy.

That year in the fall, Martin stood at the threshold of Knowledge, aching for the hills of his youth, filled with memories of his family, unprepared for the momentous challenges ahead of him. Still, this was the opportunity of a lifetime and so, with a heavy heart and life-sized dreams, he walked through the old arched doorway and never looked back.

Student Name _____ Date _____

Blue Whale

The largest living thing to ever inhabit planet Earth is not a gigantic lizard or	15
dinosaur from ancient times, but rather a grayish-blue gentle giant from the present	28
known as the blue whale. These massive mammals measure seventy to eighty feet in	42
length, which is about the length of three school buses, and they can weigh as much	58
as 150 tons. That's what twenty-five elephants would weigh! Pumping almost ten tons	71
of blood throughout the blue whale's body, its heart alone is as large as a small car.	88

The blue whale is toothless; as an alternative, though, a row of approximately	101
320 baleen plates hang from the roof of its mouth. Baleen, which is wide, black,	116
and bristlelike, is made of keratin, the same protein material our fingernails and	129
hair are made of. When a blue whale feeds, it fills its mouth with up to five tons	147
of water, engulfing vast clouds of shrimplike krill and small fish. Having forced	160
the water out of its mouth through its baleen, the whale licks the plankton off	175
with its fleshy tongue. It's estimated that 2,200 pounds of plankton are necessary to	189
satisfy a blue whale's appetite every day. It's astonishing that blue whales grow to	203
be enormous by feeding on some of the ocean's smallest creatures. Blue whales	216
spend the warm summer months feeding in the cold Arctic or Pacific waters. As the	231
weather turns cold, the blue whales migrate south to warmer waters.	242

Throughout history, blue whales have been hunted for their prized baleen,	253
blubber, meat, and bones. During the 1930s to 1960s, they were greedily	265
overhunted to dangerously low numbers and nearly became extinct. Then, various	276
laws were passed to protect the blue whale from hunting whalers. Today, the blue	290
whale is still classified as an endangered species struggling to make a comeback.	303

Fluency Test

☐ – ☐ = ☐ (wcpm)

Running Record

Oral Reading Accuracy: Reading Rate:

☐ – ☐
——————— x 100 = ☐ %
☐

☐
——— x 60 = ☐ (wpm)
☐

Blue Whale

The largest living thing to ever inhabit planet Earth is not a gigantic lizard or dinosaur from ancient times, but rather a grayish-blue gentle giant from the present known as the blue whale. These massive mammals measure seventy to eighty feet in length, which is about the length of three school buses, and they can weigh as much as 150 tons. That's what twenty-five elephants would weigh! Pumping almost ten tons of blood throughout the blue whale's body, its heart alone is as large as a small car.

The blue whale is toothless; as an alternative, though, a row of approximately 320 baleen plates hang from the roof of its mouth. Baleen, which is wide, black, and bristlelike, is made of keratin, the same protein material our fingernails and hair are made of. When a blue whale feeds, it fills its mouth with up to five tons of water, engulfing vast clouds of shrimplike krill and small fish. Having forced the water out of its mouth through its baleen, the whale licks the plankton off with its fleshy tongue. It's estimated that 2,200 pounds of plankton are necessary to satisfy a blue whale's appetite every day. It's astonishing that blue whales grow to be enormous by feeding on some of the ocean's smallest creatures. Blue whales spend the warm summer months feeding in the cold Arctic or Pacific waters. As the weather turns cold, the blue whales migrate south to warmer waters.

Throughout history, blue whales have been hunted for their prized baleen, blubber, meat, and bones. During the 1930s to 1960s, they were greedily overhunted to dangerously low numbers and nearly became extinct. Then, various laws were passed to protect the blue whale from hunting whalers. Today, the blue whale is still classified as an endangered species struggling to make a comeback.

NAME _____ DATE _____

Scott Foresman
Benchmark Test
Unit 1
Loyalty and Respect

Glenview, Illinois
Boston, Massachusetts
Chandler, Arizona
Upper Saddle River, New Jersey

ISBN-13: 978-0-328-53758-7
ISBN-10:   0-328-53758-6

1 2 3 4 5 6 7 8 9 10 V011 19 18 17 16 15 14 13 12 11 10
CC1

ISBN-13: 978-0-328-53758-7
ISBN-10:   0-328-53758-6
EAN
9 780328 537587
90000 >

PART 1: COMPREHENSION

*D*irections

When Marcie realizes that the vacant lot next to her building could be used to help the whole neighborhood, she and her friend David get to work. Read how adopting a can-do attitude helps Marcie and David help others. Then do Numbers 1 through 11.

Not Defeated Yet!

Marcie Kennedy lived in the yellow brick apartment building next to the Victory Garden—that is, it used to be the Victory Garden. Over time, it had become the Defeated-by-Weeds Garden. That's what Marcie's friend David Lopez called it anyway. The lot adjacent to Marcie's building had long been littered with weeds and debris, including a pile of cardboard boxes and old tires. Marcie strolled past it every day, barely seeing it.

One day, David asked, "What was this place, anyway? I mean, what's a Victory Garden?"

Marcie vaguely recalled the explanation her grandfather had given her. "During World War II, farms couldn't produce enough vegetables to feed people at home and the soldiers overseas, so people returned to growing their own. In neighborhoods like this one, they turned vacant lots into gardens, with everyone pitching in to help. They felt as if they were being patriotic—helping with the war effort—so people called them Victory Gardens. My great-grandparents helped start this one and my grandparents and their friends kept it going for a long time—until several years ago."

"Why did they stop?" asked David.

"Granddad says people didn't have the time anymore, but I think they just needed organization. Someone to be in charge, you know."

As David bounced his basketball against Marcie's building, they considered the weedy lot. "Our neighbor in the house next door to us has a garden," said David. "Mr. Wong was an enthusiastic gardener. He always had more fresh food than he could eat, so he shared it with people who were too busy to grow their own. The peaches he gave us were unbelievably juicy! He fell and broke his hip last year, though. Now his garden looks a lot like this one."

"I'll bet you miss those peaches," said Marcie.

"Yeah," replied David. "I'll bet Mr. Wong does too."

Marcie recalled her grandfather's face as he had described their neighborhood garden. It seemed that he missed the companionship of his neighbors as much as he missed having fresh vegetables. "You know, David," she said thoughtfully, "we could get the Victory Garden going again, with a little help."

The idea appealed to David. "I'll talk to Mr. Wong and find out what we should do to bring this garden back to life."

Mr. Wong still seemed feeble, but he was thrilled about reincarnating the Victory Garden. First, he drew plans, asking questions about the size and shape of the lot. Next, he wrote instructions for preparing the soil. Finally, he gave David a list of plants that would produce well in their region.

While David was learning, Marcie and her grandfather went door-to-door, enlisting volunteers. By mid-afternoon, they had found eleven neighbors who wanted to work on the garden. Marcie's goal was to find twelve volunteers. "If one more person pledges to help, we'll have a sufficient number," she told her grandfather.

"Then our task is complete," said Granddad, "because I want to help."

Considering the hard work and fatigue ahead, Marcie sat back in her chair and sighed. The first steps were already behind them, though. "This is going to be terrific!" she said.

"Yes, it is," agreed Granddad. "Thank you for getting it started."

1 **How did Marcie feel about the Victory Garden at the beginning of the story?**

A She didn't think about it much.

B She wished someone would clean it up.

C She enjoyed playing there.

D She remembered fondly how it used to be.

2 Which detail from the selection shows that Marcie was good at organizing?

   F   She lived in a yellow brick building.

   G   She told David the story of the Victory Garden.

   H   She quickly found twelve people to help.

   J   She wanted to eat freshly grown vegetables.

3 In what way were Marcie and David's homes similar?

   A   Neither Marcie nor David lived in a city.

   B   Both lived in apartment buildings.

   C   Neither Marcie nor David had any neighbors.

   D   Both lived next door to a neglected garden.

4 Why did Marcie want to recreate the Victory Garden?

   F   She wanted her grandfather to be happy.

   G   Mr. Wong needed her help.

   H   David thought it was an exciting idea.

   J   She enjoyed fresh peaches.

5 Which detail shows that the selection took place in modern times?

   A   Soldiers fought overseas.

   B   Marcie got help from many of her neighbors.

   C   Mr. Wong's garden was overgrown with weeds.

   D   The Victory Garden was created during World War II.

6 Which detail from the first paragraph best helps readers picture the lot?

   F   *yellow brick apartment building*

   G   *Victory Garden*

   H   *cardboard boxes and old tires*

   J   *Marcie strolled past it.*

7 **Mr. Wong's garden probably became weedy because**

   A   his injury prevented him from working in it.

   B   he was too busy helping with the Victory Garden.

   C   no one ever took the extra vegetables he grew.

   D   he got tired of growing so many fruits and vegetables.

8 **What was the *main* goal of the characters in the selection?**

   F   to eat fresh fruit and vegetables

   G   to ask Mr. Wong for advice

   H   to find twelve volunteers for the garden

   J   to bring the Victory Garden back to life

9 **Marcie believed that her grandfather missed**

   A   being in charge of things.

   B   working alongside his neighbors.

   C   the peaches that Mr. Wong grew.

   D   the excitement of his childhood.

10 **What did Marcie believe was the reason why people stopped working in the Victory Garden?**

   F   People were too busy to garden.

   G   They needed someone to keep them organized.

   H   There were not enough volunteers to do the work.

   J   Mr. Wong had broken his hip.

11 **How had Marcie's feelings changed by the end of the story?**

   A   She was getting worried about finding helpers.

   B   She didn't want her grandfather to help.

   C   She was full of dread about passing the empty lot.

   D   She had become excited about the garden.

Directions

Write your answer to Question A on the lines below. Base your answer on the story "Not Defeated Yet!"

A How would the story change if it took place in a farm community instead of a city? Use details from the story to explain your answer.

_____

_____

_____

_____

_____

_____

_____

_____

_____

Directions

Learn about one woman's mission to house and rehabilitate bats, and to give people a clearer understanding of these harmless and interesting creatures. Then do Numbers 12 through 22.

The Texas Bat Woman

In the summer of 1989, in the north Texas town of Mineral Wells, heat radiated up from the sidewalk. Outside the furniture store that she ran with her mother, a young woman named Amanda Lollar spotted something on the hot pavement. It was a bat! Her first reaction was to leave it where it lay, but something about the tiny creature tugged at her heart. It was so small and seemed so helpless. In the end, Lollar nudged it onto a newspaper with her toe, wrapped it up, and carried it home.

But how does one care for a bat? What kind of food would it eat? Did it need medicine? Lollar found answers to these questions over time, learning by trial and error. She named the bat Sunshine, and as it healed from an injury, Lollar bonded with it—she even wrote a book about Sunshine, and developed deep feelings of respect and concern for bats in general.

Bats became Lollar's passion. In the family furniture store, she treated injured bats that people found around their homes, and she took in bats that were unwisely chosen as pets, and then given up. In 1994, she founded Bat World, a nonprofit group devoted to the rehabilitation of bats.

GO ON

Mineral Wells had its share of bats. The town lay on the annual migration path for Mexican free-tailed bats, a species that arrives in the spring and has pups in the attics and eaves of old buildings. One of those buildings went up for sale, and its owner planned to have an exterminator get rid of bats that were living there. To save them, Bat World bought the building and called it Wild Sanctuary. Soon, large numbers of mother bats traveled there every spring to have pups. Bat World runs a bat hospital, too, where they treat injured bats and orphaned bat pups. Their original goal was to return all the animals to the wild, but that hasn't always been possible—some bats have had to stay on at Wild Sanctuary.

Along the way, Amanda Lollar has become a well-known expert on bats and bat care, and she is always glad to share her knowledge. When school groups visit Bat World on field trips, students learn the truth about these often misunderstood animals. For example, bats are not blind, as many people believe. They can see in daylight, and some can navigate in darkness. They use auditory clues—echoes of high-pitched sounds that they send out—to locate objects in the dark. Bats don't tangle themselves in people's hair, either; in fact, bats do a lot of good for people. Some species eat mosquitoes and insects that damage crops. A large colony of bats can devour many tons of bugs in a single night. Bats also help farmers and gardeners by pollinating plants and spreading seeds.

At Bat World, Amanda Lollar teaches people what to do if they encounter an injured bat. A person finding a hurt bat can call a wildlife rehabilitator—someone with special training in animal rescue—to deal with the animal. A list of these people, along with excellent facts about bats, can be found on the Internet.

12 **Based on the selection, which of the following is a way that bats help humans?**

F eating harmful insects at night

G living in empty buildings

H migrating over north Texas

J locating objects by echoes

13 **The main reason that Lollar has given tours of Wild Sanctuary to people is to explain**

A what to do if they find a bat.

B how bats benefit humans and nature.

C how to heal injured bats.

D what wildlife rehabilitators do.

14 Which sentence from the selection is a statement of *only* fact?

F It was so small and seemed so helpless.

G Some bats have had to stay on at Wild Sanctuary.

H Bats became Amanda's passion.

J A list of these people, along with excellent facts about bats, can be found on the Internet.

15 Based on information in the selection, what do bats have in common with people?

A They can see well in darkness.

B They can live in tall buildings.

C They don't like living in large groups.

D They use sound to find objects in the dark.

Read the diagram. Then answer Number 16.

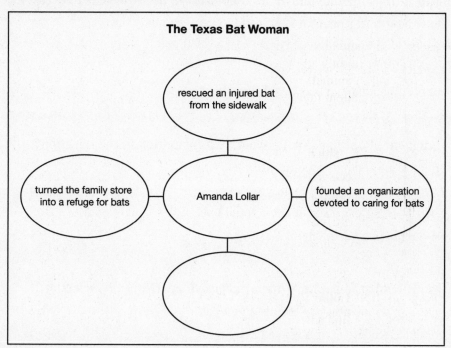

The Texas Bat Woman

- rescued an injured bat from the sidewalk
- turned the family store into a refuge for bats
- Amanda Lollar
- founded an organization devoted to caring for bats

16 What information belongs in the blank oval?

F enjoys buying fruit for bats

G likes being the boss

H feels strongly about helping bats

J lives in a small Texas town

GO ON

17 **Based on information in the selection, which statement of opinion is valid?**

A Amanda Lollar is the world's greatest expert on bats.

B Helping bats is an easy job.

C Anyone can teach the public about bats.

D Bats are important to the environment.

18 **How do wild bats likely enter and exit the building called Wild Sanctuary?**

F They fly through open windows and parts of the roof.

G They squeeze through cracks in the window and door frames.

H Workers bring them in and out in cardboard boxes each night.

J Amanda Lollar opens the front door to let them in and out.

19 **Why did the author include information about how many insects bats eat?**

A to show how hard it was for Bat World to keep so many bats fed

B so readers will know that bats don't make good pets

C so readers will feel sorry for bats

D to support the idea that bats benefit people

20 **Which statement of opinion is supported by information in the selection?**

F Caring for injured bats requires little learning.

G Bats are not very good mothers.

H Bat World is a great place to learn about bats.

J Most people know a lot about bats.

21 **What was probably the author's main purpose for writing this selection?**

A to entertain with surprising details about bats

B to convince readers to appreciate bats

C to inform readers about one woman's mission

D to gain sympathy for the condition of bats

22 **What happened to cause Amanda Lollar to buy an old building in Mineral Wells?**

F She had too many bats in her furniture store.

G She learned that the owner planned to have the bats inside killed.

H The owner offered to sell it to her at a low price.

J Someone told her that it was on the bats' migration path.

Directions

Write your answer to Question B on the lines below. Base your answer on the two selections you have read.

B **WRITING ACROSS TEXTS**

Both Amanda Lollar, from "The Texas Bat Woman," and Marcie Kennedy, the main character in "Not Defeated Yet!" came to care about something. Describe what each person started caring about, and what caused them to do so.

_____

_____

_____

_____

_____

_____

_____

_____

_____

PART 2: VOCABULARY

Directions
Mark your answer choice for Numbers 23 through 32.

23 What is the meaning of *vaguely* in the following sentence?

Marcie vaguely recalled the explanation her grandfather had given her.

A vague once again

B more vague

C in a way that is vague

D in a way that is not vague

24 The Latin root *ann* means "year." What does *annual* mean in this sentence?

The town lies on the annual migration path for Mexican free-tailed bats.

F happening twice a year

G happening every other year

H happening all within one year

J happening every year

25 In the following sentence, what do the endings of *healed* and *bonded* show?

She named the bat Sunshine, and as it healed, Amanda bonded with it.

A actions that happened in the future

B actions that happened in the present

C actions that happened in the past

D actions that happened in the past and present

26 Read this sentence from "Not Defeated Yet!"

"If one more person pledges to help, we'll have a sufficient number," she told her grandfather.

The ending *-s* in *pledges* shows an action

F that may happen.

G that is happening again.

H that happens in the past.

J that is happening right now.

27 What is the suffix in *reaction*?

A re

B act

C ion

D react

28 The Latin root *aud* means "to hear." What is the meaning of *auditory* in this sentence?

They use auditory clues to locate objects in the dark.

F having to do with sound

G moving

H having to do with light

J nearby

29 In the third paragraph of "The Texas Bat Woman," what is the meaning of *passion*?

A least favorite thing

B largest expense

C biggest problem

D greatest interest

Read this thesaurus entry for *feeble*. Then answer Number 30.

---

feeble *adj.* 1. weak, puny, frail 2. simple, simple-minded 3. low, soft, whispered 4. useless, worthless

---

30 Which word from the thesaurus entry would best replace *feeble* in the following sentence?

Mr. Wong still seemed feeble, but he was thrilled about reincarnating the Victory Garden.

F simple

G weak

H low

J useless

GO ON

Read this thesaurus entry for *debris*. Then do Number 31.

---

debris *n.* 1. ruin, remains, wreck 2. pieces, parts 3. junk, trash

---

31 Which word from the thesaurus entry would best replace *debris* in the following sentence?

The lot adjacent to Marcie's building had long been littered with weeds and debris, including a pile of cardboard boxes and old tires.

A ruin

B wreck

C parts

D junk

32 Which words in the first paragraph of "Not Defeated Yet!" help the reader understand what the word *adjacent* means?

F lived in

G past it

H used to be

J next to

PART 3: WRITING CONVENTIONS

Directions
Mark your answer choice for Numbers 33 through 40.

33   **Which sentence is written correctly?**
- **A**   Kent is visiting his Grandmother.
- **B**   We are going to visit Dr. Murphy.
- **C**   Our next speaker is miss Amelia Panzetta.
- **D**   How many States have you visited?

34   **Which sentence is written correctly?**
- **F**   The Author's name was Cecilia T. Slater.
- **G**   Lisa is going with Mom to the gym.
- **H**   Please send the bill to post office Box 655.
- **J**   Who has ever been to lake Superior?

For Numbers 35 through 40, read each sentence. Mark the answer that describes the underlined words.

35   **Work a little faster, please.**
- **A**   declarative sentence
- **B**   interrogative sentence
- **C**   imperative sentence
- **D**   exclamatory sentence

36   **Mai will give her report before George does.**
- **F**   simple subject
- **G**   complete subject
- **H**   simple predicate
- **J**   complete predicate

37   **Some sixth-grade students have won the awards.**
- **A**   simple subject
- **B**   complete subject
- **C**   simple predicate
- **D**   complete predicate

38 Do you want to stay longer since Theo just came?

    F   compound sentence

    G   complex sentence

    H   compound-complex sentence

    J   simple sentence

39 Dora will leave <u>after her mom gives a speech.</u>

    A   compound sentence

    B   complex sentence

    C   dependent clause

    D   independent clause

40 <u>Cedric's aunt is a teacher, and his uncle is a lawyer.</u>

    F   compound sentence

    G   complex sentence

    H   dependent clause

    J   independent clause

PART 4: WRITING

<table>
<tr><td>

PROMPT

Think about a time in your life when you decided to help an animal, another person, or your community. What happened to make you feel that you should help? What did you do? Were you able to make a difference? How did you feel afterward?

Write a story about your experience helping others. Include details to show how you felt before and after.

</td></tr>
</table>

<table>
<tr><td>

CHECKLIST FOR WRITERS

_____ Did I think about a time when I decided to help someone or something?

_____ Did I take notes about my story before I started writing?

_____ Did I tell my story in the order in which it happened?

_____ Did I use words and details that clearly express my ideas?

_____ Do my sentences make sense?

_____ Did I check my sentences for proper grammar and punctuation?

_____ Did I check my spelling?

_____ Did I make sure my paper is the way I want readers to read it?

</td></tr>
</table>

GO ON

18

NAME _____ DATE _____

Scott Foresman
Benchmark Test
Unit 2
Space and Time

Glenview, Illinois
Boston, Massachusetts
Chandler, Arizona
Upper Saddle River, New Jersey

ISBN-13: 978-0-328-53759-4
ISBN-10:   0-328-53759-4

1 2 3 4 5 6 7 8 9 10 V011 19 18 17 16 15 14 13 12 11 10
CC1

ISBN-13: 978-0-328-53759-4
ISBN-10:   0-328-53759-4

*D*irections
Read about the people of the Sea Islands, off the southeast coast of the United States, and their culture, which traces its history back to Africa in the 1600s. Then do Numbers 1 through 11.

The Gullah of the Sea Islands

Nearly a thousand islands hug the coast from Georgetown, South Carolina, to just north of Jacksonville, Florida. They are known as the Sea Islands. In the 1600s and 1700s, many West Africans were enslaved and brought to the islands and coastal areas. These enslaved Africans worked on plantations, or very large farms. In fields that produced rice, cotton, and a plant used for dye called indigo, the enslaved Africans built a culture and a way of life that was purely their own. They mixed English words with words from their homelands, creating a new language. The language, along with the people and their culture, became known as Gullah.

After the Civil War in the United States ended, many Gullah people who were freed from slavery bought the land in the Sea Islands where they had been working. Much of it was swampy and infested with mosquitoes. Few others wanted to live there. The only way on or off the islands was by boat, so the Gullah people remained isolated. Land on the Sea Islands passed from generation to generation. So did Gullah culture.

Gullah traditions flourished well into the second half of the twentieth century. The people on the island lived peacefully in close communities. They often sang traditional songs and gathered around storytellers to hear stories from the past. Gullah stories often include colorful animal characters that outsmart each other to get what they want. To support themselves, Gullah people farmed and fished. Some made their living from crafts, such as beautifully woven baskets and fishnets. Gullah baskets are famous among art collectors. They are usually made from sweetgrass that grows near the ocean. These baskets were once used for cleaning rice and carrying cotton. Their design can be traced all the way back to Africa.

In the mid-1900s, bridges were built from the mainland to some of the Sea Islands. Real estate developers arrived. They saw great possibilities for resorts and new neighborhoods on the peaceful islands. Many local people sold their land to developers and left. Taking their places was a growing number of people from the mainland. Old traditions began to fade. Fewer and fewer local children spoke Gullah.

For many, these changes were hard to accept. The Gullah people have traditionally valued their land and culture. Land symbolized freedom. Their language, art, and stories belonged uniquely to them. Gullah people remaining on the Sea Islands felt their way of life was in danger. Community leaders responded by organizing the annual Gullah Festival to help preserve their culture.

The Gullah Festival was first held in Beaufort, South Carolina, in 1987, and it continues today. Visitors eat mouthwatering seafood gumbo and other traditional dishes. They stroll through arts and crafts exhibits, and listen to marching bands. African dance companies move to the rhythms of traditional music, jazz groups, and gospel choirs. Above all, the Gullah Festival revolves around the history, music, food, language, and people of the Sea Islands.

1 **The Gullah Festival was started mainly to**

A persuade outsiders to learn the Gullah language.

B celebrate the joining of the Sea Islands with the mainland.

C maintain the traditions of the Gullah way of life.

D encourage residents of other states to travel to South Carolina.

2 **What generalization is supported by information in the selection?**

F No one speaks the Gullah language anymore.

G Most Gullah people are descended from West African people.

H Bridges now connect all the Sea Islands.

J Most visitors to the Gullah Festival buy a sweetgrass basket.

3 **Which statement correctly compares the Gullah language and English?**

A The Gullah language was spoken in the 1600s, but English was not.

B People of the Sea Islands speak Gullah, but not English.

C Gullah contains elements of English, but English has no elements of Gullah.

D The Gullah language is older than English.

4 **The Gullah people lived by themselves for many years mainly because**

F the islands where they lived were not easy to reach.

G their leaders wanted it that way.

H their language was hard for visitors to understand.

J they had no time to do anything but work.

5 **What is the most likely purpose of the map?**

A to give readers an idea of the size and location of the Sea Islands

B to show people traveling from other states the best routes to Beaufort

C to help students learning about the early history of South Carolina

D to show where enslaved Africans came from in the 1600s and 1700s

6 **How is modern Gullah culture different from the Gullah culture of the early 1900s?**

F Modern Gullah people weave baskets from sweetgrass.

G More people from the mainland live among the Gullah.

H Gullah stories no longer include animal characters.

J Modern Gullah fishers weave their own fishing nets.

7 According to the selection, what part of Gullah culture traces its design directly back to Africa?

A bridges connecting the islands

B marching bands

C the Gullah Festival

D baskets woven from sweetgrass

8 Which graphic source would best help readers learn about Gullah traditions?

F photographs of visitors at past events

G diagrams that show how sweetgrass baskets are made

H a chart showing the number of visitors at each festival since 1987

J a time line showing major events in the history of South Carolina

9 A bridge from the mainland to one of the Sea Islands most likely would have been completed in

A 1667.

B 1787.

C 1887.

D 1967.

10 What is the main idea of the selection?

F Gullah sweetgrass baskets are valued by collectors.

G Storytellers are important in Gullah culture.

H The Gullah culture developed on the Sea Islands and elsewhere.

J Time and development have changed life for the Gullah people.

11 Based on the selection, which of the following most likely happened first?

A The first Gullah Festival was held.

B The first real estate developer arrived on a Sea Island.

C The first sale of Sea Island land to a developer took place.

D The first bridge from the mainland to a Sea Island was built.

GO ON

Write your answer to Question A on the lines below. Base your answer on "The Gullah of the Sea Islands."

A   Explain how Gullah culture changed in the mid-1900s. Tell what happened to bring about change and describe how Gullah people responded.

_____

_____

_____

_____

_____

_____

_____

_____

Directions
Robert Dominguez tells the story of how, through luck and fate, he became a mariachi musician. Read his story. Then do Numbers 12 through 22.

Mariachi Musician in Michigan

   History has a funny way of repeating itself. Take me, Robert Dominguez, for example. I grew up in Lansing, Michigan, about 1,500 miles from Mexico. I never spoke Spanish when I was young. I never even *heard* Spanish except when my mom talked long distance to her mom—my grandmother—who lived in South Texas. Because my grandmother lived so far from Lansing, I never got to know her well.

   If I had, I might have found out about her brother, my great-uncle, much earlier. He had been a well-known mariachi musician in Mexico. I am an example of how history, once again, has repeated itself. Despite growing up far away from Mexico and its culture, I'm a mariachi musician too, although I'm not well-known. But Mr. Montoya, the director of the university mariachi orchestra I've joined, says that I play the *guitarrón* with talent. (It's the instrument that looks like a huge guitar and provides the bass line.)

GO ON

So how did a kid in Michigan end up as a *guitarrón* player? I'll tell you. I took regular guitar lessons for several years. But I never really felt inspired. Then, when I was thirteen, I went to San Antonio, Texas, to visit my cousin. He was a trumpet player in his school's mariachi band. He dragged me to a mariachi festival. I say "dragged" because I was expecting to be bored. Instead, the music was fascinating. Something in my blood responded to the syncopated rhythms of mariachi music. I also got caught up in the swirling sense of competition among the bands.

I left that festival feeling a little sad. I didn't think I would ever have the opportunity to play in a mariachi band in Lansing.

However, luck was with me. During my first year in high school, the Spanish teacher and the orchestra director started a mariachi band. Two years of serious instruction and frequent rehearsals followed. Then we were ready to compete. We won prizes at several festivals. We even played at Disney World during my senior year.

After I joined the band and got my own *guitarrón*, my mom told me about her uncle, my grandmother's brother. He had played the violin in a mariachi orchestra that became famous in his home state of Jalisco, in Mexico. Last year, my mom's cousin sent me a tattered photo of my great-uncle Ramón. It's amazing how little the outfit of mariachis has changed in fifty years.

Sometimes during a performance, I find myself wishing my grandmother and great-uncle could see me. I think they would have liked this particular repetition of history.

MARIACHI FACTS

- Originally, mariachi music was played only by rural people; it gained popularity in all regions and cities of Mexico in the 1930s.

- Instruments in a typical mariachi band include 6 to 8 violins, 1 guitar, 3 trumpets, 1 *guitarrón* and 1 *vihuela* (a five-stringed instrument that resembles a small guitar).

- The standard uniform is a waist-length jacket and pants or skirt, both decorated with large silver buttons.

- A musical form called *son* is commonly played by mariachi groups; the popular song "La Bamba" is an example.

---

12 **What happened before the narrator went to San Antonio to visit his cousin?**

F He learned that his great-uncle was a mariachi musician.

G He attended a mariachi festival and competition.

H He learned to play the *guitarrón*.

J He took regular guitar lessons.

13 **What was the narrator's first experience with mariachi music?**

A playing in a high school mariachi orchestra

B learning about his great-uncle, a famous mariachi musician

C attending a mariachi festival with his cousin

D playing *guitarrón* in a university mariachi orchestra

8

14 How was the narrator's experience similar to that of his cousin?

   F Both played in high school mariachi bands.

   G Both played trumpet in their high school bands.

   H Both attended high school in Lansing, Michigan.

   J Both took Spanish classes in high school.

15 Which detail best demonstrates the narrator's pride in his Mexican ancestry?

   A He wished that his grandmother could see him play the *guitarrón*.

   B Since his grandmother lived far away, he never got to know her well.

   C He responded to the syncopated rhythms of mariachi music.

   D His orchestra director said that he played the *guitarrón* with talent.

16 According to the selection, what did the narrator and his great-uncle have in common?

   F the skill level they developed

   G the age at which they began to perform

   H the type of musical instrument they played

   J the clothing they wore during performances

17 From the information in the "Mariachi Facts" section, readers can conclude that

   A a tourist in Mexico in 1920 probably would not have heard mariachi music.

   B "La Bamba" is the most popular song that mariachi musicians play.

   C mariachi musicians are required to have silver buttons on their uniforms.

   D there are always eight violins in a mariachi band.

18 Which sentence from the selection supports this generalization?

There were few mariachi bands in Michigan.

   F History has a funny way of repeating itself.

   G I didn't think I would ever have the opportunity to play in a mariachi band in Lansing.

   H We won prizes at several festivals.

   J He had played the violin in a mariachi orchestra that became famous in his home state of Jalisco, in Mexico.

GO ON

19 What is the second paragraph mostly about?

  A how well the narrator played the *guitarrón*

  B how little the narrator knew about his Mexican relatives

  C why the narrator did not hear about his great-uncle earlier

  D why the narrator was an example of history repeating itself

20 Which of the following best describes the information in the "Mariachi Facts" section?

  F clues to understanding the story

  G reasons to become a professional musician

  H suggestions for further study

  J background about the subject of the story

21 Based on the selection, what is a valid generalization that readers can make about mariachi?

  A All mariachi festivals include a competition among bands.

  B Mariachi festivals are held daily at Disney World.

  C Mariachi music was once popular in most parts of Mexico.

  D Jalisco is the place to hear the best mariachi music.

22 According to the selection, most of the instruments in mariachi bands are

  F brass instruments.

  G string instruments.

  H inherited from family.

  J played while seated.

*D*irections

Write your answer to Question B on the lines below. Base your answer on the two selections you have read.

B

WRITING ACROSS TEXTS

Both "The Gullah of the Sea Islands" and "Mariachi Musician in Michigan" deal with the importance of something from the past to people living today. Describe how people in these selections connect with the past, and why past-to-present connections might be important. Use details from the selections to support your answer.

_____

_____

_____

_____

_____

_____

_____

_____

_____

PART 2: VOCABULARY

Directions
Mark your answer choice for Numbers 23 through 32.

23 What is the meaning of *resembles* in the following sentence?

A vihuela is a five-stringed instrument that resembles a small guitar.

A costs as much as

B looks like

C is better than

D is louder than

24 Which sentence shows the base word of *competition* without a suffix?

F He was a competent trumpet player.

G They showed competence, not greatness, with their music.

H Then we were ready to compete.

J Their band was a major competitor.

25 The Latin word *insulatus* means "made into an island." Based on this information, what is the meaning of *isolated* in the following sentence?

The only way on or off the islands was by boat, so the Gullah people remained isolated.

A snobbish

B unique

C talented

D cut off

26 What guide words are on the dictionary page where the word *flourish* is found?

F found—fourth

G flax—fluctuate

H flop—flounder

J flood—floor

27 What suffix or suffixes can be found in the word *peacefully*?

A *-ful* and *-ly*

B *peace-* and *-fully*

C *-ly* only

D *peace-* only

28 What is the meaning of *purely* in this sentence?

The Africans built a culture and a way of life that was purely their own.

F too pure

G not pure

H becoming pure again

J in a way that was pure

Use these entries from a dictionary to answer Numbers 29 through 31.

> **bass**[1] (bās) *n., pl.* **bass • es** **1** the range of the lowest voice in music **2** a singer with similar range **3** an instrument with similar range **– adj.** **4** of, or having the range of a bass voice or instrument
>
> **bass**[2] (bas) *n., pl.* **bass** or **bass • es** **1** any of several freshwater fishes related to sunfish, popular as game and food **2** any of similar fishes living in saltwater

29 According to the dictionary entries, the word *bass* can be used as which two parts of speech?

A noun and verb

B adverb and verb

C adjective and preposition

D noun and adjective

30 Which definition of *bass* is used in this sentence?

The guitarrón looks like a huge guitar and provides the bass line.

F bass[1], definition 1

G bass[1], definition 2

H bass[1], definition 4

J bass[2], definition 1

31 Which definition for *bass* is used in this sentence?

When my uncle and I were at the lake, he caught a largemouth bass.

A bass[1], definition 1

B bass[2], definition 1

C bass[1], definition 3

D bass[1], definition 2

GO ON

32   The Latin root *volvo* means "to turn." What is the meaning of *revolves* in this sentence?

Above all, the festival revolves around the history, music, food, language, and people of the Sea Islands.

F   centers

G   jumps

H   speaks

J   rules

Q.2
Exam

PART 3: WRITING CONVENTIONS

Directions

Mark your answer choice for Numbers 33 through 40.
For Numbers 33 and 34, choose the word or words that best complete the sentence.

33 Next year Keith _____ karate lessons.

   A had taken

   B will take

   C has taken

   D did take

34 Which sentence includes a linking verb with a predicate nominative?

   F Andrew's attitude is the problem.

   G Trisha and Jo Lynn felt proud.

   H Hernando seems pretty tired.

   J Our best players have been hurt.

35 Which sentence is written correctly?

   A All of the tomato are perfectly ripe.

   B The photos are in a box in the garage.

   C How many sister-in-laws do you have?

   D The oxes were yoked together.

36 Which sentence is written correctly?

   F The doctor as well as the nurse are late.

   G Is all the people in the group ready?

   H They wants to learn how to ice-skate.

   J Nobody in our family plays tennis.

37 Which sentence is written correctly?

   A The womens' contests are next.

   B Caitlins finger's seem swollen.

   C Have you read Lucys' poems?

   D The horses' stalls were dirty.

GO ON

38   Which sentence is written correctly?

   F   Either Paul or Rob have to clean up.

   G   Both Chris and Pat knows how to ski.

   H   All the doors in the house are wooden.

   J   Emilia and Marta is moving to Alaska.

39   Which sentence is written correctly?

   A   Six sheriffes work in this county.

   B   Did you bring knifes and forks?

   C   Both series of events were important.

   D   Omar and Rose do not like strawberrys.

40   Which sentence is written correctly?

   F   These paintings' belong to Mr. Fernandez.

   G   Hannah Willis writes children's books.

   H   The Johnson'es house is on the corner.

   J   Womens clothing is on the fifth floor.

PART 4: WRITING

PROMPT

Imagine that your teacher has given you an assignment to research a member of your family who lived at least fifty years ago, and then to write a report based on your findings. What are the steps you would need to take to learn about that family member?

Write a how-to report on what those steps would be. Do not simply list the steps. Include details that would be helpful to anyone who reads your report to find out how to research his or her own family history.

CHECKLIST FOR WRITERS

_____ Did I think about the steps I would need to take to write my report?

_____ Did I take notes about the importance of each step?

_____ Did I write my explanation in the order in which the steps are done?

_____ Did I use words and details that clearly express my ideas?

_____ Do my sentences make sense?

_____ Did I check my sentences for proper grammar and punctuation?

_____ Did I check my spelling?

_____ Did I make sure my paper is the way I want readers to read it?

18

Benchmark Test Unit 2

6 Copyright © Pearson Education, Inc., or its affiliates. All Rights Reserved.

NAME _____   DATE _____

Scott Foresman
Benchmark Test
Unit 3
Challenges and Obstacles

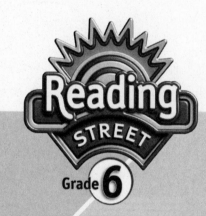

Glenview, Illinois
Boston, Massachusetts
Chandler, Arizona
Upper Saddle River, New Jersey

ISBN-13: 978-0-328-53760-0
ISBN-10:   0-328-53760-8
1 2 3 4 5 6 7 8 9 10 V011 19 18 17 16 15 14 13 12 11 10
CC1

ISBN-13: 978-0-328-53760-0
ISBN-10:   0-328-53760-8

EAN

9 780328 537600

Directions
Read the story of Gerhard and Rosamund and the peach seed that finally brought them together. Then do Numbers 1 through 11.

The Peach Seed

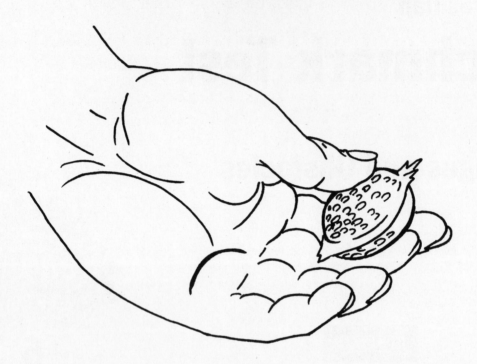

There once was a man named Gerhard, who made his living as a thief. He was so skillful that he had never been caught. One day, Gerhard saw Rosamund, the bookseller's assistant. He immediately fell in love and began to court her. When he was sure of her love, he confessed to Rosamund how he made his living. Gerhard asked Rosamund to marry him and promised to become an honest man if she would have him.

"Yes," she replied, "but to prove that you've changed, you must acquire my wedding ring through honest work."

Gerhard agreed. The next day, he began working as a stonecutter's helper, but the job was boring. He soon told himself, "This one last time, I'll resort to theft. After that, I'll find a better occupation."

Unfortunately, while stealing a ring for Rosamund, Gerhard was caught and thrown into the royal dungeons. Each afternoon, a guard passed food through Gerhard's cell bars: moldy bread, rotten meat, and a piece of spoiled fruit. One day, as Gerhard bit into a bruised but still sweet peach, an idea blossomed in his mind. He carefully cleaned the peach seed and wrapped it in a cloth. To the guard, he shouted, "I have a valuable gift for the king."

The guard was doubtful, but he escorted the prisoner to the castle anyway. Gerhard bowed before the king and said, "Your Majesty, I bring you a wondrous gift."

But when Gerhard presented the peach seed, the king bellowed, "You ridicule me! Five more years in the dungeons for you!"

Gerhard chose his next words carefully. "Your Majesty, please take a moment to reconsider. What if I told you that this is a magic peach seed? What if I also told you that when planted by an honest person who has never stolen anything, the seed will produce a tree that bears fruit of solid gold? For anyone else—for a scoundrel like myself—the tree will produce only ordinary fruit. Would you accept the gift of such a peach seed?"

The king blushed and stammered, "I . . . I must decline. My memory is not as sharp as it once was, and it's possible that I did something foolish in my youth." He offered the peach seed to his son.

The prince, recalling all the peasants whose land he had stolen, said, "I . . . I . . . I'm not a farmer, and I have no interest in planting seeds." The king then offered the seed to his most trusted general.

"I . . . I . . . depart for battle on the morrow," the general mumbled, contemplating all the lives he had taken.

After an awkward silence, the king pronounced, "Prisoner, you have taught us all a lesson more valuable than gold. You've paid for your crime. For this worthwhile instruction, I grant you your freedom."

Gerhard bowed and thrust the peach seed in his pocket. There he kept it for the remainder of his life. On his deathbed, he gave the seed to his and Rosamund's son, along with the conviction that honesty brings great rewards.

1 **What was the first thing that caused Gerhard's way of life to change?**

A going to prison

B meeting with the king

C seeing Rosamund

D working for a stonecutter

2 **What is the most likely reason that Gerhard waited until he was sure of Rosamund's love to tell her that he was a thief?**

F He was afraid she would not fall in love with a thief.

G He was planning to steal from her boss, the bookseller.

H He wanted time to earn money for a wedding ring.

J He was afraid she would tell the king's guards he was a thief.

GO ON

3 What best explains the king's first reaction to the peach seed?

A He did not want to talk to a prisoner.

B He felt insulted by the gift of the peach seed.

C He thought anything magic was nonsense.

D He knew that Gerhard was trying to trick him.

4 Gerhard's plan depended most upon

F the peach seed being magical.

G the king having lied in the past.

H the general being loyal to the king.

J Rosamund loving Gerhard.

5 Gerhard most likely kept the peach seed in his pocket to remind him of

A the importance of his wife and son.

B the first time he saw Rosamund.

C the lesson that he had taught the king.

D the time he spent in prison.

6 After getting out of prison, which of these did Gerhard believe was most important?

F cleverness

G honesty

H riches

J interesting work

7 What did Rosamund want Gerhard to do for her?

A stop being a thief

B prove he was smarter than the king

C learn how to be a stonecutter

D steal a wedding ring

8 What goal did Gerhard maintain throughout the story?

F to gain his freedom from jail

G to have Rosamund as his wife

H to teach the king a lesson

J to work for the stonecutter

9 Why did Gerhard get a job as a stonecutter's helper?

   A to hide from the king's guards

   B to work closer to Rosamund's store

   C to learn where the stonecutter kept his gold

   D to show Rosamund that he could change

10 What caused Gerhard to be arrested?

   F He tried to trick the king.

   G He was caught stealing a ring for Rosamund.

   H He left his job as a stonecutter.

   J He took Rosamund away from the bookseller.

11 What happened after Gerhard was thrown into prison?

   A He decided to marry Rosamund.

   B He stole a wedding ring.

   C He found a job helping the stonecutter.

   D He bit into a bruised peach.

GO ON

Write your answer to Question A on the lines below. Base your answer on "The Peach Seed."

A   How do you think Gerhard's attitude about stealing changed while he was in prison? Use details from the story to support your answer.

_____

_____

_____

_____

_____

_____

_____

_____

Wilma Rudolph

On the summer day in 1940 when Wilma Rudolph was born, her mother, Blanche, must have been worried. The baby had come sooner than she should have and weighed only four and a half pounds. The Rudolph family already had nineteen children. Although they worked hard, money was tight. This girl, because she was premature and so small, would surely have health problems, Blanche probably thought.

GO ON

Blanche was right. Tiny Wilma suffered from pneumonia, scarlet fever, and polio, all before her fifth birthday. She nearly died, but didn't, although the polio had left her left leg twisted. For years, Wilma wore a brace on that leg.

Despite their troubles, the Rudolph family was close. Wilma's brothers and sisters took turns massaging her leg each day. Between her job and caring for her other children, Blanche took her daughter to a hospital for weekly treatments.

Wilma's health problems were as much a challenge to Wilma as a disability. After the brace came off when she was nine, Wilma was determined to be "normal" like her brothers and sisters. It wasn't long before she was playing basketball, just like them. For a while, Wilma had to wear a special shoe, but by high school, the shoe had gone the way of the leg brace. Along with her sister, Wilma made the high school basketball team. She lived and breathed competition. She became the school's star player and set scoring records in her home state of Tennessee.

Wilma's playing caught the eye of Ed Temple, a track coach at Tennessee State University. He asked Wilma to his summer sports camp, where she retrained as a runner. She was so impressive that the university later offered her a scholarship. Coach Temple also encouraged her to train for the Olympics. Just as she had always done, Wilma set a goal for herself and went after it. In 1956, at the Olympics in Melbourne, Australia, sixteen-year-old Wilma was there. She ran as fast as the wind, earning a bronze medal for the United States. Afterward, she continued to train hard. Her sights were set on the 1960 Olympics in Rome, Italy.

In Rome, Wilma Rudolph became a world-class runner. Fans loved her. Almost six feet tall, she was graceful and lovely as well as fast. Everywhere she went, people cheered and crowded near, anxious to see her and to hear her soft, calm voice. They pounded the side of her bus, so she would wave at them. On the track, Wilma flew across finish lines. She set world records and took home three gold medals, more than any American woman before her. People called her "the fastest woman in the world." Wilma Rudolph's determination to be "normal" had taken her way beyond anything she had ever expected.

12 **As a young child, Wilma Rudolph was**

F always fast.

G often sick.

H never unhappy.

J usually on the race track.

13 When Wilma was born, what did Blanche, her mother, most likely worry about?

A that Wilma would hurt herself if she went to the Olympics

B that Wilma might not fit in with the rest of the family

C that there was no time to get to the hospital for the birth

D that Wilma would have health problems as a child

14 According to the selection, what happened after Wilma stopped using her leg brace?

F Her brothers and sisters gave her a party.

G She developed scarlet fever.

H She played basketball on the school team.

J Her left leg became twisted.

15 Why did young Wilma go to a hospital every week?

A to help others who had polio

B to receive treatments for her leg

C so she wouldn't catch pneumonia again

D so her mother could learn to care for her

16 What sentence from the selection suggests that Wilma's brothers and sisters were also athletic?

F It wasn't long before she was playing basketball, just like them.

G Despite their troubles, the Rudolph family was close.

H Wilma's brothers and sisters took turns massaging her leg each day.

J The Rudolph family already had nineteen children.

17 Why did track coach Ed Temple invite Wilma to his summer sports camp?

A Watching her play basketball, he recognized her talent.

B She was the fastest runner on her high school track team.

C She told him that she wanted to run in the Olympics.

D When he saw her run in Rome, he knew that she was fast.

18 Based on the selection, which conclusion about Ed Temple is valid?

F He was probably the Olympic track coach in 1956.

G He was probably an old friend of the Rudolphs.

H He probably trained Wilma Rudolph to race.

J He probably played basketball in college.

GO ON

19 **When did people start calling Wilma Rudolph "the fastest woman in the world"?**

A when they saw how fast she was on the basketball court

B at the 1960 Olympics in Rome, Italy

C when she ran track for the University of Tennessee

D at the 1956 Olympics in Melbourne, Australia

20 **After the 1956 Olympics, Wilma Rudolph's *main* goal was to**

F race well at the 1960 Olympics in Rome, Italy.

G make the Italian fans love her.

H be the first woman to win an Olympic gold medal.

J visit the historic sites in Rome, Italy.

21 **Which detail from the selection supports the generalization that people loved Wilma Rudolph?**

A She set records in Tennessee.

B Fans pounded the side of her bus.

C She set herself a goal and went after it.

D At the age of twenty, she was almost six feet tall.

22 **What generalization about Wilma Rudolph is supported by information in the selection?**

F Any time she competed in a race, she won.

G She never slowed down, even when she was sick.

H Every member of her family was a fast runner.

J She always worked hard to achieve her goals.

Directions

Write your answer to Question B on the lines below. Base your answer on the two selections you read.

B Both Gerhard in "The Peach Seed" and Wilma Rudolph faced challenges and, in the end, gained important rewards. Discuss the challenges each person faced, and how each benefited from getting past them.

PART 2: VOCABULARY

Directions
Mark your answer choice for Numbers 23 through 32.

23 Read this sentence from "The Peach Seed."

The guard was doubtful, but he escorted the prisoner to the castle anyway.

The ending **-ed** shows that **escorted** refers to

A an action that happens in the future.

B an action that happens for the second time.

C an action that is happening now.

D an action that happens in the past.

24 What is an antonym for *skillful* as it is used in this sentence?

He was so skillful that he had never been caught.

F smart

G ordinary

H untrained

J expert

25 In the following sentence what does *acquire* mean?

You must acquire my wedding ring through honest labor.

A obtain

B repair

C exchange

D create

26 What is the meaning of *occupation* in the third paragraph of "The Peach Seed"?

F interest

G excuse

H method

J job

27 What is the meaning of *wondrous* as it is used in the following sentence?

Gerhard bowed before the king and said, "Your Majesty, I bring you a wondrous gift."

A feeling wonder

B having the quality of wonder

C without wonder

D having too much wonder

28 In this sentence, what does the ending *-ing* in *massaging* suggest?

Wilma's brothers and sisters took turns massaging her leg each day.

F an action that is continuous or repeated

G an action that happens for the second time

H an action that happens in the future

J an action that happens in the past and the present

29 In this sentence from "Wilma Rudolph," what is the meaning of *disability*?

Wilma's health problems were as much a challenge to Wilma as a disability.

A something that makes her less able

B something that makes her able again

C something that makes her better able

D something that makes her overly able

30 In this sentence, what is the meaning of *retrained*?

Wilma retrained as a runner.

F trained for too long

G did not train

H trained all over again

J trained too little

31 What is an antonym for *impressive* as it is used in this sentence?

She was so impressive that the university later offered her a scholarship.

A   hardworking

B   forgettable

C   tall

D   excited

32 What is the suffix in *determination*?

F   *deter-*

G   *determine-*

H   *de-*

J   *-ation*

PART 3: WRITING CONVENTIONS

Directions
Mark your answer choice for Numbers 33 through 40.

For Numbers 33–34, read each sentence. Mark the answer that describes the underlined word in each sentence.

33 The principal gave <u>Terry</u> an award.

   A direct object

   B indirect object

   C predicate adjective

   D predicate subject

34 Before the play, Margo seemed <u>sure</u> of herself.

   F direct object

   G indirect object

   H subject complement

   J predicate adjective

35 Which sentence is written correctly?

   A Ms. Lee's class already had began the lesson.

   B Mr. Mora threw the ball over Evita's head.

   C The dog seen the cat before I did.

   D Amelia done the best job of all.

36 Read the sentence.

Tired and aching, the runner dropped the team's baton.

Which sentence has the same meaning as the sentence above?

   F The tired, aching team dropped the runner's baton.

   G The tired, aching runner was dropped by the team.

   H The team's baton was dropped by the tired, aching runner.

   J The team's tired, aching runner was dropped by the baton.

37 Which sentence is written correctly?

   A Ivan and Marco should of run faster.

   B I've ate too many bananas at one time.

   C Richard has already came and gone.

   D Casey's parents have bought her a dog.

GO ON

38   Which sentence is written correctly?

    F   Yesterday Leticia laid in bed until ten.

    G   The moon makes the tide rise and fall.

    H   Lucy set at a big table all alone.

    J   I wish you would learn me how to skate.

39   Which sentence includes a transitive verb?

    A   Yesterday, Yoshiko swung his little cousin.

    B   Curt went to the beach for two weeks.

    C   The puppy on the left has already eaten.

    D   Emily cried because her shirt was torn.

40   What is the main verb in this sentence?

The dog's fur, matted and dripping from the rain, smelled like dirty socks.

    F   is

    G   matted

    H   dripping

    J   smelled

PART 4: WRITING

PROMPT

In everyone's life, some things are easy to do, and some things are more difficult. In an essay, compare and contrast something you have done that was easy for you to do and something else that was more difficult for you to do. Include details about both experiences, and describe how you felt about the experiences.

CHECKLIST FOR WRITERS

_____ Did I think about something that was easy for me to do and something that was more difficult?

_____ Did I take notes for my paper about the two experiences?

_____ Did I use words and details that clearly express my ideas?

_____ Do my sentences make sense?

_____ Did I check my sentences for proper grammar and punctuation?

_____ Did I check my spelling?

_____ Did I make sure my paper is the way I want readers to read it?

NAME _____ DATE _____

Scott Foresman

Benchmark Test

Unit 4
Explorers, Pioneers, and Discoverers

PEARSON

Glenview, Illinois
Boston, Massachusetts
Chandler, Arizona
Upper Saddle River, New Jersey

ISBN-13: 978-0-328-53761-7
ISBN-10:   0-328-53761-6

1 2 3 4 5 6 7 8 9 10 V011 19 18 17 16 15 14 13 12 11 10
CC1

ISBN-13: 978-0-328-53761-7
ISBN-10:   0-328-53761-6

90000>

EAN

9 780328 537617

PART 1: COMPREHENSION

Directions

Bridges are not just functional; they are testaments to our aspiration to build. Read about the history of the Brooklyn Bridge. Then do Numbers 1 through 11.

Emily Roebling and the Building of the Brooklyn Bridge

When the Brooklyn Bridge was completed in 1883, it was the eighth wonder of the world. What was so special about it? It spanned the East River and connected two of the fastest-growing cities in the world, Brooklyn (yes, it was considered a separate city then) and New York City. It was the longest and tallest bridge ever built—so amazing that many had thought it would be impossible to build.

The problem was that the bridge had to go across one of the world's busiest rivers. A lofty bridge was required so that tall ships could pass under it. That meant it had to be a suspension bridge. A suspension bridge has cables—strong, thick ropes of steel—supporting the deck, or main part, of the bridge. The cables stretch between tall towers. No one had ever built such a big bridge before.

Bridges are built by engineers. These skilled workers draw the plans and direct the construction. The chief engineer of the Brooklyn Bridge was John Augustus Roebling. Roebling was famous for building the world's two biggest bridges at that time. He was the first person to think that a bridge across the East River was possible. However, building bridges was daring and dangerous. Soon after work began in 1869, Roebling died as a result of an accident. He was one of twenty men who died during construction because of fire, accidents, and disease.

Roebling's son, Washington Roebling, became chief engineer. Washington had helped his father design the bridge and had also supervised the construction of the two beautiful stone towers. He was the best person to take over.

Yet tragedy struck again. In 1872, Washington Roebling became ill with caisson disease. This sickness is caused by spending too much time in a caisson, an underwater chamber filled with compressed air. Although he was sick, Washington continued to direct construction. He watched the work from the window of his Brooklyn home. His wife, Emily Roebling, studied math and engineering, subjects that women did not learn at that time. She began visiting the construction site and supervising the work. She remained in charge for the next eleven years.

There were many setbacks during the construction. A large fire burned for several weeks. A cable came apart and fell into the river. The builders received tons of faulty steel cable that had to be replaced. In 1882, Washington's job was in danger because he could not leave home. Emily Roebling made a speech defending him. Making speeches was another thing that women did not do at that time.

The Brooklyn Bridge was completed in 1883, a symbol of the greatness of New York and the ingenuity of the United States. President Chester Arthur opened the bridge, and Emily Roebling was the first person to ride across it. Thousands followed her on the most exciting day of the bridge's history.

Since then, millions of people have crossed it. The bridge is known for both its usefulness and its loveliness, and to this day it carries cars, walkers, and cyclists between Brooklyn and Manhattan, two great sections of New York City.

1   **According to the selection, which event happened first?**

A   Washington Roebling became chief engineer.

B   Emily Roebling made a speech.

C   A cable came apart and fell into the river.

D   John Roebling died.

GO ON

2 Which of the following words from the second paragraph is a clue to a cause-and-effect relationship?

F problem

G had

H busiest

J so

3 Why did Washington Roebling become chief engineer?

A He had completely designed the bridge.

B He was the most qualified person.

C He got sick during construction.

D His wife was able to help him.

4 Which of the following is a statement of opinion?

F The Brooklyn Bridge is a suspension bridge.

G The Brooklyn Bridge spans the East River.

H Thousands followed her on the most exciting day of the bridge's history.

J Making speeches was another thing that women did not do at that time.

5 Emily Roebling can best be described as

A determined.

B concerned.

C inflexible.

D imaginative.

6 Why were cables so important to the construction of the Brooklyn Bridge?

F Cables take the place of steel.

G Cables are fireproof.

H The Brooklyn Bridge has stone towers.

J The Brooklyn Bridge is a suspension bridge.

7 What is the main idea of the sixth paragraph?

A Builders used faulty steel cable that had to be replaced.

B A cable came apart and fell into the East River.

C Problems slowed the construction of the bridge.

D Washington Roebling almost lost his job.

8 **After reading the selection, you can generalize that**

F the Brooklyn Bridge is still the largest in the world.

G Emily Roebling was an unusual woman in her time.

H Washington Roebling designed many more bridges.

J most famous bridges were built in the 1870s.

9 **Which of the following is a conclusion about life in the 1870s that you can draw from the selection?**

A People were not paid well for their work.

B Women did not take jobs as engineers.

C Automobiles had already been invented.

D There were many types of bridges in the United States.

10 **The main reason that the author wrote this selection was to**

F persuade people to learn more about bridges in New York City.

G explain how suspension bridges are designed and constructed.

H express an opinion about John and Washington Roebling.

J describe Emily Roebling's role in building the bridge.

11 **Washington Roebling became ill**

A because he suffered from the death of his father.

B after being injured in a fire that burned for several weeks.

C because of the effects of being in an underwater chamber.

D due to the stress of the many setbacks to construction.

GO ON

Directions

Write your answer to Question A on the lines below. Base your answer on "Emily Roebling and the Building of the Brooklyn Bridge."

A What qualities helped the Roebling family build the bridge that became "the eighth wonder of the world?" Use details from the selection to support your answer.

_____

_____

_____

_____

_____

_____

_____

_____

*D*irections

Neal's family vacation takes place during a stretch of bad weather. Read about the things Neal and his friends and family do at the beach. Then answer Numbers 12 through 22.

Neal Writes a Letter

222 Beach Way
Ocean City, CA 92000
July 12, 2011

Dear Grandma,

Greetings from the beach! I hope you and Grandpa are well. As you know, we're all at the beach. I wanted to tell you everything that has happened during our vacation.

First, I should let you know who is here. In addition to me, Mom, Dad, and Lily, there are two others. Lily's friend Jennifer and my friend Roger are both staying with us. Roger and I will both go to Roosevelt Middle School in the fall.

We have been here nearly two weeks now. I have to say that this has been a challenging vacation. I don't mean to complain, but we've encountered many obstacles to having fun. Dad calls them "challenges." For one thing, it has rained nearly every day. I don't mean just normal drizzly rain. I mean deluges, complete with thunder and lightning. The weather has kept us inside the house almost the whole time.

GO ON

After playing board games, going to the movies, and fixing up the house for ten days, everyone became a little restless. I love to snorkel and build things on the beach, so I felt frustrated. Somehow we all kept our spirits up, and Mom says that is important.

The sun came out for the first time yesterday, and Lily, Jennifer, Roger, and I immediately ran to the beach. It was terrific—for about two hours. Lily and Jennifer spent the whole time lying on beach towels and talking. But Roger and I managed to construct an elaborate city out of sand. We built skyscrapers, a hospital, a city hall, and even a bridge over a moat. We used some pieces of driftwood to make the bridge because, of course, sand won't hold up by itself.

We were proud of the sand city—even Lily and Jennifer were impressed with our feats of sand engineering, and they admired our hard work and ingenuity. However, almost the second we finished construction, it began to rain again. And it didn't just drizzle—the sky let loose with torrents of water. Needless to say, the city was demolished, and there was no chance later in the day for us to reconstruct it.

Lily did manage to take a picture of the sand city, which we had named Oceanica before the storm blew in, and I'm enclosing the snapshot in this letter so you can see what it looked like. I know you always like to see the projects I work on. I hope you like this one.

Naturally it has rained all morning so far. But it looks as if we'll be able to go out soon. Therefore, I'll finish this letter now and put it in the mailbox on my way to the beach. I miss you and Grandpa. I look forward to seeing you as soon as we get home.

Your grandson,
Neal

12 **According to the fourth paragraph, everyone felt restless because they**

F   were trapped indoors.

G   were forbidden to go to the beach.

H   spent too much time on the beach.

J   hated playing board games.

13 **What happened as a result of the rain?**

A   Neal's letter got wet.

B   Neal's sand city was destroyed.

C   Lily took a picture of the sand city.

D   Neal used driftwood for a bridge.

14 What happened while the sun was out?

    F   Neal wrote a letter to his grandmother.

    G   The sand city was destroyed.

    H   The four kids played board games.

    J   The four kids went to the beach.

15 Which event happened last in the selection?

    A   The family played board games.

    B   The kids ran to the beach.

    C   Lily took a picture of the sand city.

    D   The family went to the movies.

16 Which of the following words from the last paragraph is a clue to a cause-and-effect relationship?

    F   Naturally

    G   But

    H   Therefore

    J   soon

17 Where did the events in the selection take place?

    A   in Ocean City

    B   in Neal's home in the city

    C   in Oceania

    D   in Neal's grandmother's house

18 Neal's feelings toward his grandmother can best be described as

    F   careless.

    G   warm.

    H   regretful.

    J   timid.

GO ON

19 Based on the selection, one way that Neal and Roger differ from Lily and Jennifer is that the boys like to

A build things.

B take pictures.

C go snorkeling.

D play board games.

20 Why did the author probably decide to write this selection as a letter?

F to use vivid language to describe Neal's experiences

G to show how each member of the family felt

H to describe the vacation in the greatest detail

J to limit the information to Neal's point of view

21 The reader can tell that Neal's mother and father

A regretted having made the trip to the beach.

B welcomed the sunny weather as much as the kids did.

C enjoyed making the sand city with the boys.

D encouraged the kids to have a positive attitude.

22 The author's purpose in writing this selection was to

F entertain with details of a vacation.

G persuade people to spend time at a beach.

H explain how to build a sand city.

J express an opinion about family vacations.

Directions

Write your answer to Question B on the lines below. Base your answer on the two selections you have read.

B In both selections, people built something. Describe the materials each set of builders used and some challenges each faced while building. Give details or examples from both selections to explain your answer.

WRITING
ACROSS
TEXTS

_____

_____

_____

_____

_____

_____

_____

_____

_____

_____

PART 2: VOCABULARY

*D*irections
Mark your answer choice for Numbers 23 through 32.

23 What is the meaning of *spanned* in the following sentence?

The Brooklyn Bridge spanned the East River and connected Brooklyn and New York.

A tunneled under

B drained out from

C measured around

D stretched across

24 What is the meaning of *lofty* in the following sentence?

A lofty bridge was required so that tall ships could pass under it.

F long

G high

H strong

J beautiful

Use this entry from a dictionary to answer Numbers 25 through 27.

ca•ble (kā´ bəl), **1** *n.* a strong, thick rope, usually made of wires twisted together: *A suspension bridge hangs from strong steel cables.* **2** *n.* an insulated bundle of wires that carries an electric current or electric signals. **3** *n.* cable TV: *We watched a movie on cable.* **4** *n.* cablegram. **5** *v.* (earlier) to send a message across the ocean by underwater cable: *They cabled us from Paris.* ☐ *v.* **ca•bled, ca•bling**.

25 According to the dictionary entry, the word *cable* can be used as which two parts of speech?

A verb and adjective

B noun and adverb

C noun and verb

D adjective and noun

26 Which dictionary meaning of *cable* is used in the following sentence?

A cable came apart and fell into the river.

F definition 1

G definition 2

H definition 3

J definition 4

27 What is the dictionary meaning for *cable* as it is used in the following sentence?

The telephone company used a flag to mark the underground cable.

A definition 1

B definition 2

C definition 3

D definition 4

28 What is the meaning of *reconstruct* in the following sentence?

Needless to say, the city was demolished, and there was no chance later in the day for us to reconstruct it.

F build correctly

G build again

H build carefully

J build ahead of time

29 What are the guide words for the page in the dictionary on which the word *frustration* is found?

A fry—fulcrum

B frosted—fruit

C frontal—frugal

D frumpy—fudge

30   What is the meaning of *deluges* in the following sentence?

> *I don't mean just normal drizzly rain. I mean deluges, complete with thunder and lightning.*

F   downpours

G   disasters

H   sprinkles

J   winds

31   What is the meaning of *elaborate* as it is used in the following sentence?

> *Roger and I managed to construct an elaborate city out of sand, with many buildings, houses, streets, and a bridge.*

A   simple

B   complicated

C   clean

D   stony

32   Which meaning of *projects* is used in the following sentence?

> *I know you always like to see the projects I work on.*

F   group of apartment buildings

G   school assignments

H   makes one's voice to carry over a distance

J   ideas and plans

PART 3: WRITING CONVENTIONS

Directions

Mark your answer choice for Numbers 33 through 40.

33   Which of the following words can be used as a subject pronoun?

   A   her

   B   him

   C   them

   D   she

34   Which of the following sentences is written correctly?

   F   Larry said he would play softball.

   G   How do your know when to study?

   H   Emilio would like it, if her was home.

   J   Oliver thought his would return.

35   Which of the following sentences is written correctly?

   A   Is he the one whom sings?

   B   Who did Linda expect?

   C   Shelly welcomed Judy, who was her cousin.

   D   Please give the book to anyone whom wants it.

36   What is the antecedent of *it* in the following sentence?

The day we spent at the beach was long, but then it ended on a happy note.

   F   day

   G   we

   H   beach

   J   note

37   Which of the following sentences is written correctly?

   A   Zhu walked to the counter and tapped it.

   B   Patrick took the tests and passed it.

   C   Simone lifted the water and drank them.

   D   Alberta picked up the disc and threw them.

GO ON

38 **Which of the following is an indefinite pronoun?**

F yourself

G them

H anyone

J this

39 **Which sentence uses a possessive pronoun correctly?**

A Who's house is this?

B This room will be your's.

C The backpack is mine, not Roger's.

D The sweaters on the shelf are their's.

40 **Which sentence is written correctly?**

F Sam studied hisself in the mirror.

G They did the chores theirselves.

H Eduardo wants to finish the work himself.

J Frank and Alice rode to the meet themselfs.

STOP

PART 4: WRITING

PROMPT

"Emily Roebling and the Building of the Brooklyn Bridge" describes an engineering challenge. In "Neal Writes a Letter," people and characters have to deal with bad weather, which Dad calls a challenge. Think of a time when you faced a challenge. Write a story about the challenge you faced and what you did to overcome it. Remember to include details.

CHECKLIST FOR WRITERS

_____ Did I think about a challenge that I faced and overcame?

_____ Did I include details about the challenge and what I did to overcome it?

_____ Did I organize my ideas before I began to write?

_____ Did I use words and details that clearly express my ideas?

_____ Do my sentences make sense?

_____ Did I check my sentences for proper grammar and punctuation?

_____ Did I check my spelling?

_____ Did I make sure my paper is the way I want readers to read it?

NAME _____ DATE _____

Scott Foresman
Benchmark Test
Unit 5
Resources

Glenview, Illinois
Boston, Massachusetts
Chandler, Arizona
Upper Saddle River, New Jersey

ISBN-13: 978-0-328-53762-4
ISBN-10:   0-328-53762-4

ISBN-13: 978-0-328-53762-4
ISBN-10:   0-328-53762-4

1 2 3 4 5 6 7 8 9 10 V011 19 18 17 16 15 14 13 12 11 10
CC1

*D*irections
Lexie finds some interesting things to do during her summer vacation and learns an important lesson at the same time. Read the story, and then do Numbers 1 through 11.

Lexie Lends a Hand

"I have nothing to do this summer," Lexie whined. It was the first day of vacation, and she was eating breakfast with her two older brothers. "Most of my friends are going away, and I'll be left here all by myself—no one to hang out with, nothing fun to do, and nothing useful to accomplish. Older kids can get jobs or do volunteer work, but I'm too young to do anything valuable or interesting."

Seventeen-year-old Aaron listened to her grumbling and groaning for a while. "Enough!" he said. "Let's think of this a different way. Instead of focusing on what you don't have, let's consider what you want and how you might be able to get it."

"Kids my age never get what they want," Lexie complained.

"Kids your age can start looking out for themselves," said fourteen-year-old Dan. "I hate to admit it, but Aaron's right. You're looking only at what you don't have. What do you have? What do you like to do, and what are you good at?"

"I like little kids and dogs," Lexie said immediately, "but I'm too young to babysit, and I haven't taken the Red Cross baby-sitting course yet. I'm also too young to volunteer at the animal shelter."

- -

"Those are both great things," said Aaron. "Let's think about them one at a time. You probably are a little too young to baby-sit, but maybe you can take the Red Cross certification course this summer so you'll be ready when you're old enough."

"I really like that idea," replied Lexie. "I'll call the Red Cross and find out when the course is being given."

Soon Lexie was enrolled in a week-long baby-sitting course at the local Red Cross headquarters. Each day she learned interesting things about children and how to care for them. She learned what toys and games are appropriate for babies and children of different ages, what to do in an emergency, and even how to act at a job interview. Most fascinating of all, she learned how to administer CPR to infants, children, or adults who stopped breathing. Lexie felt very grown-up and accomplished. She wanted to use her new skills to help people.

On the last day of class, as she waited for Aaron to pick her up, Lexie glanced idly at the pamphlets in the Red Cross office. Two caught her eye. One described how to plan for the care of pets during disasters, and the other gave information about first aid for injured pets. Lexie read both with great interest and learned a lot she didn't know before—for example, most emergency shelters won't accept pets, so people must plan ahead for safe places to take their cats and dogs if a flood or hurricane happens.

"Excuse me, please," Lexie said to the receptionist in the Red Cross office. "Do you have any more of these brochures? I'd like to hand them out to my friends and neighbors." There was no touch of whining in her voice, and she spent the last weeks of her vacation busy with a new and exciting project.

1 **Which of the following events occurred first in the story?**

A Lexie learned how to administer CPR.

B Lexie complained to her brothers.

C Lexie enrolled in a baby-sitting class.

D Lexie found out about disaster relief.

2 Which action got Lexie started toward solving her problem?

F She complained to her brothers.

G She took a baby-sitting class.

H She called the Red Cross.

J She read some pamphlets.

3 Why was Lexie unable to get a summer job?

A She was too young to work.

B She did not know what kind of job she wanted.

C No one in her family could give her a ride.

D Her parents would not allow her to work.

4 What main problem did Lexie have in the first three paragraphs of the story?

F She missed her friends.

G She was quarreling with her brothers.

H She was thinking negatively.

J She needed to earn money.

5 What is this selection mostly about?

A helping animals

B caring for children

C looking for opportunities

D learning from brothers

6 The author probably wrote this selection to

F persuade readers to work for the Red Cross.

G teach an important lesson in an amusing way.

H show the importance of disaster planning.

J describe the baby-sitter certification course.

7 What happened as a result of Lexie's conversation with her brothers?

A Lexie took a baby-sitting class.

B Lexie became a baby-sitter.

C Dan volunteered at the animal shelter.

D Aaron helped by handing out brochures.

8 Which of these problems was resolved by the end of the selection?

   F   Lexie was too young to volunteer at the animal shelter.

   G   Lexie's neighborhood emergency shelter did not accept pets.

   H   Lexie's friends were all away for the summer.

   J   Lexie had nothing to do all summer.

9 In the eighth paragraph, why did Lexie feel grown-up and accomplished?

   A   She had taken a course with many grown-ups.

   B   She had gone to the Red Cross office by herself.

   C   She had learned how to care for pets during disasters.

   D   She had learned things that would let her help people.

10 Which of the following is the best statement of the theme of the selection?

   F   Helping animals can be very rewarding.

   G   People may have talents they are not aware of.

   H   Brothers can help you learn about yourself.

   J   Everyone should do some kind of volunteer work.

11 How did Lexie change from the beginning to the end of the selection?

   A   She learned how to take action to get what she wanted.

   B   She learned how to think positively about her brothers.

   C   She discovered how much she liked helping people.

   D   She learned that she should listen to her brothers.

GO ON

Directions

A   Describe the events that led to Lexie getting what she wanted. Use examples from the selection to support your answer.

_____

_____

_____

_____

_____

_____

_____

Directions

Yo's family has a magic cat! Read about how the cat provides for Yo's daughters while Yo is away from home. Then do Numbers 12 through 22.

Rice from a Cat's Fur
A Retelling of a Korean Folk Tale

Many centuries ago, there lived in Korea a brilliant scholar by the name of Yo, who was so intelligent that the Queen herself named him minister of the court to advise her on crucial matters. Yo was a kind and generous person, but when he became absorbed in his duties at court, he frequently neglected to manage his own daily affairs. He routinely gave away so much rice to beggars who came to his house that his three daughters were often left with almost no rice in the storeroom.

However, Yo's family managed to get along. Then one day Yo was instructed to go to China to persuade the Chinese Emperor to assist the Korean Queen. When they heard about his new duty, Yo's daughters became anxious. China was far away, and they wondered how they would be able to survive during their father's extended absence. The eldest daughter told Yo, "We only have one jar of rice left in the storeroom. How will we have enough to eat while you are away on this long voyage?"

GO ON

Yo considered the situation and looked down at the family cat, which was a gentle creature with smooth, black fur. This cat was somewhat unusual in that he never blinked or slept; he would simply loll about the house with his eyes wide open. "Don't worry," said Yo, as he picked up the cat and stroked its fur from its tail up its back toward its head. "If you rub the cat's fur in this backward manner, he will give you all the rice you need."

The daughters were not particularly comforted by this advice, but they bade their father a fond farewell, and as the months passed during his absence, they managed to survive. To purchase more food after the storeroom was emptied, they sold many of their possessions, including fine chests and silver hairpins. Then one day they ran out of everything they could sell.

"What should we do?" asked the middle daughter. Unfortunately, none of the daughters could remember how to get the cat to produce rice. They tried singing it songs and giving it a bath, but none of these efforts worked. Finally, one day the youngest daughter happened to pick up the cat and rub its fur backward, and she discovered that the cat did indeed yield rice. Lovely white grains piled up in mounds on the floor.

Soon the sisters had enough rice to eat and to sell, and they were able to buy back all of the possessions they had sold. After three years, Yo returned home to find his daughters in good spirits and health, and he learned that the magical cat had provided well for them.

Because he had been successful in negotiating help from the Chinese Emperor, Yo had been richly rewarded by the Queen, and he declared that the family would never again need to resort to getting rice from the cat. Although the youngest daughter still rubbed the cat's fur this way and that, the cat only purred and stared at her with unblinking eyes.

12   **There was little rice in the storeroom for Yo's daughters to eat because**

F   their cat ate most of the rice.

G   they forgot to go to the store.

H   Yo gave much of the rice to beggars.

J   the Queen did not pay Yo for his work.

13   **What happened when the youngest daughter rubbed the cat's fur backward?**

A   The cat ran away from the house.

B   The cat made a pile of rice.

C   The cat began to blink its eyes.

D   The cat told her where to find rice.

14 What happened as a result of Yo's successful negotiations with the Chinese Emperor?

F Yo was able to buy rice.

G Yo decided to stay in China.

H The Queen rewarded Yo with riches.

J The Emperor gave Yo a chest of rice.

15 Which of the following is a clue word from the fourth paragraph that shows sequence?

A but

B Then

C particularly

D including

16 The author probably wrote this story to

F make fun of the three daughters' behavior.

G express an opinion about irresponsible fathers.

H describe life in Korea many centuries ago.

J entertain with a tale about a magical cat.

17 Where did the story take place?

A in the palace of the Korean Queen

B in the palace of the Chinese Emperor

C in Yo's house in Korea

D in a storeroom

18 Yo can best be described as a

F great scholar.

G nervous parent.

H creative magician.

J generous father.

19 How was the problem resolved at the end of the tale?

A One of the daughters became the next Queen.

B Yo's family decided to grow their own rice.

C After Yo returned home, he became wealthy.

D The cat continued to feed Yo's family.

GO ON

20　**What event set the plot in motion?**

　　F　Yo returned from China.

　　G　Yo began to work for the Queen.

　　H　Yo was sent to the Chinese court.

　　J　The daughters had to sell fine chests and hairpins.

21　**What is the overall theme of the selection?**

　　A　Hard work is always rewarded.

　　B　People may get what they need in unexpected ways.

　　C　Kindness to animals is its own reward.

　　D　People who travel to faraway lands learn interesting things.

22　**What are the fourth and fifth paragraphs mainly about?**

　　F　how long the daughters had to take care of themselves

　　G　what the daughters had to sell to survive

　　H　why the youngest daughter rubbed the cat's fur

　　J　what the daughters did while Yo was away

Directions

Write your answer to Question B on the lines below. Base your answer on the two selections you have read.

B

WRITING ACROSS TEXTS

In "Lexie Lends a Hand" and "Rice from a Cat's Fur," people find a solution to a problem. Describe the problems Lexie and Yo's daughters had and how their problems were solved.

_____

_____

_____

_____

_____

_____

_____

_____

GO ON

PART 2: VOCABULARY

*D*irections
Mark your answer choice for Numbers 23 through 32.

23 **Which word is an antonym of *valuable* as it is used in this sentence?**

I'm too young to do anything valuable or interesting.

A worthless

B useful

C unusual

D difficult

24 **Which word means about the same thing as *whined* in this sentence?**

"I have nothing to do this summer," Lexie whined.

F complained

G moaned

H cried

J exclaimed

25 **Which meaning of *court* is used in this sentence?**

Yo became absorbed in his duties at court.

A a place where trials are held

B an area marked or walled off for a game

C advisers and officers of a king or queen

D to seek the affections of someone

26 **What does the word *appropriate* mean in this sentence?**

She learned what toys and games are appropriate for babies and children of different ages.

F inexpensive

G improper

H accurate

J suitable

27 Which word is an antonym of *negotiating* in this sentence?

Yo had been successful in negotiating for help from the Chinese emperor.

A battling

B discussing

C assisting

D investigating

28 What does the word *purchase* mean in this sentence?

To purchase more food after the storeroom was emptied, they sold many of their possessions.

F find

G buy

H prepare

J trade

29 Which meaning of *course* is used in this sentence?

I'll call the Red Cross and find out when the course is being given.

A the way a person chooses to act

B the direction of travel of a vehicle

C a path that something moves over

D a series of lessons on a subject

30 Which meaning of *matter* is used in this sentence?

Yo advised the Queen on a crucial matter.

F a small but definite amount

G a topic of interest or relevance

H the substance of which an object is made

J to be of importance

GO ON

31 Which word is a synonym for *yield* in the following sentence?

The cat did indeed yield rice.

A eat

B produce

C locate

D take

32 Which word is an antonym of *consider* as it is used in this sentence?

Let's consider what you want and how you might be able to get it.

F study

G argue about

H plan

J reject

PART 3: WRITING CONVENTIONS

Directions
Mark your answer choice for Numbers 33 through 40.

33 Which of the following contractions is written correctly?

A wasn't

B wer'ent

C could'nt

D isnt

34 Which of the following sentences is written correctly?

F We don't never see you anymore.

G Why don't you ever visit your grandparents?

H Ivan wanted to buy art brushes but couldn't find none.

J Sara didn't hear nothing the entire night.

35 Which of the following sentences includes a predicate adjective?

A A smart boy like Tony will do well on the test.

B Only a smart person could answer that question.

C Marta is extremely intelligent.

D Lou asked an intelligent question.

36 Which of the following sentences is written correctly?

F Several of the hispanic students in our class are from Guatemala.

G Many Japanese and Korean Families live in our town.

H Have you eaten at that Chinese restaurant?

J The new bakery sells delicious french bread.

37 Which of the following sentences is written correctly?

A These mystery books is the ones I like best.

B This here green and black backpack is mine.

C This package as well as them boxes belong to Molly.

D We just planted that rosebush over there.

38 Which of the following sentences is written correctly?

    F   My dog smells bad, but your dog smells worst.

    G   My dog Lance is the best dog in the world.

    H   My dog ate very little food, and yours ate even least.

    J   Max can run the most far of all the dogs in the neighborhood.

39 What is the adjective clause in this sentence?

    People who have a skill should teach it to someone else when they have time.

    A   to someone else

    B   who have a skill

    C   should teach it

    D   when they have time

For Number 40, mark the answer that describes the underlined words.

40 Shaundra plans to do volunteer work <u>at an animal shelter</u>.

    F   adverb clause

    G   adverb phrase

    H   adjective clause

    J   adjective phrase

PART 4: WRITING

PROMPT

In "Rice from a Cat's Fur," Yo tried to persuade the Chinese Emperor to help the Korean Queen. In "Lexie Lends a Hand," Aaron and Dan persuade Lexie to take action. Choose a topic or cause you strongly believe in. Think about how you can get others to agree with your viewpoint. You want to be convincing enough to motivate your readers to act or do something differently. Be sure to include reasons and supporting details to establish the need for change.

CHECKLIST FOR WRITERS

_____ Did I think about a cause I believe in?

_____ Did I have good reasons for what I want?

_____ Did I organize my paper in a logical way?

_____ Did I use words and details that clearly express my ideas and that can convince others?

_____ Do my sentences make sense?

_____ Did I check my sentences for proper grammar and punctuation?

_____ Did I check my spelling?

_____ Did I make sure my paper is the way I want readers to read it?

Benchmark Test   Unit 5

NAME _____ DATE _____

Scott Foresman
Benchmark Test
Unit 6
Exploring Cultures

Glenview, Illinois
Boston, Massachusetts
Chandler, Arizona
Upper Saddle River, New Jersey

ISBN-13: 978-0-328-53763-1
ISBN-10:   0-328-53763-2

1 2 3 4 5 6 7 8 9 10 V011 19 18 17 16 15 14 13 12 11 10
CC1

ISBN-13: 978-0-328-53763-1
ISBN-10:   0-328-53763-2

EAN

9 780328 537631

90000>

PART 1: COMPREHENSION

Directions

About one hundred years ago, a recent immigrant to the United States wrote this letter to his cousin living in the country he had left. Read the letter. Then do Numbers 1 through 11.

A Letter from America

Dear Cousin John,

Thank you for your letter. I am glad to know that you, your wife, and your children are well, and I am always glad to hear from my relatives. Because I came to this new land, so far away and so different from home, it makes me happy to hear news from the old country.

You tell me that life is hard for you and your family and ask me whether you should emigrate. I cannot tell you "yes" or "no," but I can tell you honestly what it is like here, and perhaps that will help you decide.

First of all, it is hard to explain how different life is here. You and your family live near a small town and know everyone you meet. Everyone speaks the same language, follows the same religion and customs, and eats similar food. I live in a huge city filled with people from around the world. I hear dozens of different languages spoken, and I cannot communicate with many of the people I meet. The streets are busy, dirty, and swarming with such a variety of people that I cannot possibly describe them.

I can buy clothing, furniture, and food from many places. Sometimes all the variety and choice is overwhelming, and I long for a life that is quiet, safe, and familiar; but most of the time my life here is fascinating.

You have probably heard that the streets in America are paved with gold and that everyone gets rich. Certainly some people succeed beyond our wildest dreams, but they do so only through years of hard work, rising from simple worker to supervisor to owner by working long and hard and saving money to eventually buy a business.

On the other hand, there is less poverty here—less chance that you will see your children go hungry. For example, I work in a factory, and I hope to become a foreman very soon. My wife also works in a factory, and because we are fortunate enough to rent a three-room apartment, we also earn money by taking in boarders. We are not wealthy, but we are never in want and we are gradually improving our lot. If you come, you could stay with us for a few weeks while you got settled.

You are now a farmer who struggles every day. Here, you would probably work in a factory. You might eventually buy land, but it would take you many years to earn enough money to do that. Certainly there are more opportunities for newcomers in the city than on the land.

For your children, some things would be better here. Not just your sons, but also your daughters could go to school, since education is free and for everyone. They might finish high school! But while in school, they will meet children from many countries— and perhaps learn some new ways that you may not like. Consider this carefully.

I hope my thoughts in this letter, which I send with affection, will help you as you make this important decision.

Your cousin,
Peter

1 **What is one way in which the places where Peter and John live are different?**

A Only Peter lives in a place with a diverse population.

B Only Peter lives in a place where everyone gets rich.

C Only Peter lives in a place where most people are farmers.

D Only Peter lives in a place where there are few schools.

2 **Based on the selection, what is an important difference between John's country and America?**

F In America, everyone must work hard.

G In America, people know all their neighbors.

H In America, girls can go to school.

J In America, people can take in boarders.

GO ON

3 **What can you conclude about Peter from the selection?**

A He has a wife and several children who all work in factories.

B He is honest and hard-working and willing to help people in need.

C He is timid and reluctant to tell people things they do not want to hear.

D He is sorry that he left his country and took his family to America.

4 **Based on the selection, why is John thinking about going to America?**

F He wants his sons to go to school.

G He wants his children to learn new ways.

H His children are starving.

J His life is hard in his country.

5 **What is the main idea of the fifth paragraph?**

A In America, the streets are paved with gold.

B In America, people who work hard can succeed.

C In America, everyone works in factories.

D In America, some people buy a business.

6 **What would be a big difference for John between life in his country and life in America?**

F In America, he would work in a city.

G In America, he would not find work.

H In America, he would live with his cousin.

J In America, he would buy a farm.

7 **What is the major idea being compared in the third paragraph?**

A the religion and customs found in each country

B the condition of the streets in each place

C the people living in each area

D the language spoken in each country

8 **Which of the following is a generalization that could be made based on the selection?**

F In America, everyone eventually gets rich.

G In America, all children want to go to school.

H In America, everyone helps newcomers get ahead.

J In America, there is greater opportunity.

9 According to the selection, if John decides to go to America, it will most likely be because he wants to

    A   get a job in a factory.

    B   live among a variety of people.

    C   buy his own farm.

    D   improve life for his family.

10 The author *probably* wrote this selection to

    F   persuade readers that history can be interesting.

    G   show what life was like for immigrants.

    H   entertain with a lively and eventful story.

    J   express an opinion about immigration.

11 Which of the following is the *best* statement of the theme of this selection?

    A   Change is difficult; it is seldom possible to make a change that will improve your life.

    B   Family ties are important, no matter where you are.

    C   Life is complicated; even when it seems good, there are drawbacks.

    D   Parents must think about their children when considering a big life change.

GO ON

Directions

Write your answer to Question A on the lines below. Base your answer on "A Letter from America."

A This selection gives many details about life for an immigrant in America. Think about a place you are very familiar with. Describe how this place is similar to and different from the world Peter described. Include details from the selection in your answer.

_____

_____

_____

_____

_____

_____

_____

_____

Two groups of Native Americans lived in eastern North America before Europeans arrived. Read about these people. Then do Numbers 12 through 22.

Native Americans: Algonquin and Iroquois

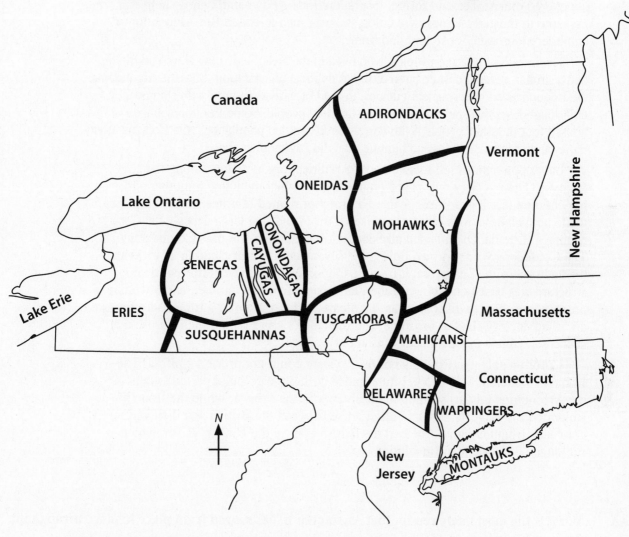

When Europeans arrived in northeastern North America, Native Americans of two distinct cultural groups lived there: Algonquin speakers and Iroquois speakers. Although they lived in similar places and had similar lifestyles, the differences between these groups were unbelievably profound. In addition, these differences led to conflicts that had an impact on the early history of the United States.

A large number of tribes speaking Algonquin languages lived in the vast woodlands between the Great Lakes and the Atlantic Ocean. Their homelands stretched from Canada in the north to Virginia in the south. Algonquins were the first Native Americans that most Europeans encountered, and their assistance as well as their resistance shaped colonial history.

The Algonquin tribes shared a culture based on farming, hunting, and fishing. Tribes living near the seashore depended on fishing for much of their diet, while inland tribes relied more on farming and hunting. All of them lived in villages of small, round houses covered in bark, hides, or mats. They made clothing out of animal skins; they made utensils of materials that included stone, wood, bark, and grasses. They moved throughout the year from farming villages to fishing, hunting, or gathering grounds.

Political structure among the Algonquins was based on the tribe, a relatively small group with a common language and territory. Sometimes powerful chiefs conquered other tribes and formed confederations—Powhatan, whose help was essential to the early Jamestown colonists, was such a leader. But Algonquin confederations were loose knit and brief.

The Iroquois-speaking peoples, who lived in the area that is now New York State, had a similar material culture but a different political organization. Like the Algonquins, the Iroquois lived in permanent villages; instead of individual family dwellings, they built longhouses that sheltered up to two hundred people. Some Iroquois villages housed four thousand people. With large, densely settled populations, the Iroquois relied more on agriculture and less on hunting than did Algonquin tribes.

Large populations led to an elaborate political organization among the Iroquois. Their society was based on the hearth, which included a mother and her children. Each hearth was part of a group of related families; several families made up a clan; various clans comprised a tribe; and five large tribes—the Cayuga, Mohawk, Oneida, Onondaga, and Seneca—made up the Iroquois Confederacy. The Confederacy was formed during the seventeenth century, and in 1715, with the addition of the Tuscarora, it became the Six Nations. The entire political structure was based on women: Inheritance came from the mother, and a woman's property was hers to dispose of as she pleased. The women of a tribe could remove an unsatisfactory chief at any time, and the chief's sister would then choose a successor. Chiefs made all decisions about warfare.

Unfortunately, the Iroquois political system could not prevent conflict. The Iroquois homeland was of vital importance during the colonial period, when the Algonquins primarily allied themselves with the French, while the Iroquois supported the English. When conflict arose between the British and their former colonists, Iroquois support helped the British control the Hudson River, which prolonged the American Revolution.

12 **What is the most likely reason that Algonquin tribes moved from place to place throughout the year?**

F   to meet the Iroquois

G   to fight the British

H   to plant crops

J   to find seasonal food

13 Based on the selection, what is the most important difference between Algonquin and Iroquois tribes?

    A The Iroquois had a more complex political structure.

    B The Iroquois were more warlike.

    C The Iroquois chiefs were usually women.

    D The Iroquois supported the French.

14 Based on the selection, which of these aspects of the Algonquins and Iroquois was most similar?

    F their food, clothing, and shelter

    G their political structure

    H their support for European colonies

    J their population size

15 Readers can conclude from the final paragraph of the selection that

    A tribal alliances were weakened during the colonial period.

    B conflict was common during the colonial period.

    C the French had an important role in the American Revolution.

    D the Iroquois political system was similar to that of the British.

16 According to the selection, which event occurred first?

    F Europeans arrived in North America.

    G Powhatan formed an Algonquin confederation.

    H Native Americans inhabited North America.

    J The Tuscarora joined the Iroquois Confederacy.

17 Which of these differences between the two groups of Native Americans is described in detail in the selection?

    A the treatment of women

    B their methods of warfare

    C their selection of a chief

    D the type of dwelling

GO ON

18   **What is the main idea of the fourth paragraph?**

    F   Powhatan helped support the Jamestown colonists.

    G   Algonquin political structure was based on individual tribes.

    H   Algonquins sometimes formed confederations of tribes.

    J   Tribes are relatively small groups of people.

19   **Which of the following is a statement of opinion?**

    A   The differences between Iroquois and Algonquins were unbelievably profound.

    B   When Europeans arrived in northeastern North America, Native Americans of two cultural groups lived there.

    C   Tribes that spoke Algonquin languages lived between the Great Lakes and the Atlantic Ocean.

    D   Algonquins were the first Native Americans that most Europeans encountered.

20   **The author probably wrote this selection to**

    F   demonstrate that the Iroquois system was superior.

    G   show how differences in culture affect history.

    H   give information about seventeenth-century America.

    J   inform the reader about colonial history.

21   **What is the third paragraph mainly about?**

    A   the diet of Algonquin tribes

    B   the lifestyle of Algonquin tribes

    C   the migration of Algonquin tribes

    D   the crafts of Algonquin tribes

22   **Which of the following conclusions about Native American life can you draw from the selection?**

    F   Finding enough food was often difficult for Native Americans.

    G   Native Americans resisted European settlement.

    H   Native Americans continually moved from place to place.

    J   Warfare was a part of Native American life.

Directions

Write your answer to Question B on the lines below. Base your answer on the two selections you have read.

B

WRITING ACROSS TEXTS

Compare and contrast "A Letter from America" and "Native Americans: Algonquin and Iroquois." In what ways are they similar? In what ways are they different? Include details from each selection.

_____

_____

_____

_____

_____

_____

_____

_____

_____

_____

PART 2: VOCABULARY

*D*irections
Mark your answer choice for Numbers 23 through 32.

23 **Which meaning of *lot* is used in the following sentence?**

We are not rich, but we are gradually improving our lot in life.

A fortune

B land

C delivery

D group

24 **What is the meaning of *swarming* in the following sentence?**

The streets are busy, dirty, and swarming with such a variety of people that I cannot possibly describe them.

F infested

G crowded

H swimming

J singing

25 **Which meaning of *simple* is used in the following sentence?**

People can rise from simple worker to supervisor to owner through hard work.

A foolish

B easy

C ordinary

D unfussy

26 **Which meaning of *ways* is used in the following sentence?**

Your children may learn some new ways that you may not like.

F possibilities

G methods

H routes

J customs

Benchmark Test   Unit 6

27 What is a synonym of *vast*, as it is used in the following sentence?

A large number of tribes speaking Algonquin languages lived in the vast woodlands between the Great Lakes and the Atlantic Ocean.

A productive

B hostile

C dense

D enormous

28 What is the meaning of *profound* in the following sentence?

Although they lived in similar places and had similar lifestyles, the differences between these groups were unbelievably profound.

F intelligent

G great

H thoughtful

J weighty

29 What is the meaning of *utensils* in the following sentence?

They made utensils of materials that included stone, wood, bark, and grasses.

A tools

B food

C clothing

D houses

30 Which meaning of *common* is used in the following sentence?

A tribe is a relatively small group with a common language and territory.

F ordinary

G widespread

H frequent

J shared

GO ON

31   What is a synonym of *conflict*, as it is used in the following sentence?

The Iroquois political system could not prevent conflict.

A   debate

B   difference

C   interference

D   warfare

32   What is the meaning of *elaborate* in the following sentence?

Large populations led to an elaborate political organization.

F   decorated

G   rich

H   work-related

J   complex

PART 3: WRITING CONVENTIONS

Directions
Mark your answer choice for Numbers 33 through 40.

33 **Which of the following sentences is written correctly?**

A By the way is Brett going to the show?

B Yes, I believe he will be there.

C Next week class we'll talk about the moons of Jupiter.

D It is my pleasure Ms. Tobin.

34 **Which of the following sentences is written correctly?**

F She asked, "Can we meet at noon?"

G Did he say, "I will be on time?"

H They wanted to know, "When the game began."

J She shouted, "I have to go now"!

35 **Which of the following sentences is written correctly?**

A The hotel is located in Los Angeles California.

B Send the letter to P.O. Box 2, Rome WA 98111.

C Charles lives at 12 Cherry Road, Lincoln, Nebraska.

D That woman is from Tokyo Japan.

36 **Which of the following sentences is written correctly?**

F Carlo sewed on a button, and Michael set the table.

G Julia ran a marathon and Sandy did yoga.

H Duong wrote a note but Jeannie did not read it.

J Merrill went to the store so, Ari wouldn't have to go.

37 **Which of the following sentences is written correctly?**

A He is tall intelligent and kind.

B She is short, smart, and nice.

C You are big friendly, and young.

D I am, small, pale, and old.

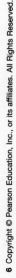

GO ON

38 Which of the following sentences is written correctly?

F Hera lifted the lid smelled the soup, and tasted it.

G They ate macaroni and cheese, bread, butter.

H Rick placed the dessert, an apple pie, on the counter.

J The main course a lasagna, took a while to make.

39 Which of the following sentences is written correctly?

A That woman, as you know is a famous scientist.

B Flavio by the way, made the team.

C Jerry, however, won't be playing this season.

D I for instance can never remember the time.

40 Which of the following sentences is written correctly?

F The doors opened and the crowd rushed inside.

G It's time to leave so check the back door.

H The sun is shining but, I can't leave the library.

J The weather changes, and so do we.

PART 4: WRITING

PROMPT

"A Letter from America" is about two people who live very different lives. Think about two people you know who live very different kinds of lives. Write an essay that tells how these two people are similar to and different from each other. Remember to include details about where each person lives, their habits, and what they like to do.

CHECKLIST FOR WRITERS

_____ Did I think about two people I know?

_____ Did I include details about how they are similar and different?

_____ Did I use words and details that clearly express my ideas?

_____ Did I organize my paper in a logical way?

_____ Do my sentences make sense?

_____ Did I check my sentences for proper grammar and punctuation?

_____ Did I check my spelling?

_____ Did I make sure my paper is the way I want readers to read it?

18

NAME _____ DATE _____

Scott Foresman
Benchmark Test
End-of-Year

Grade 6

Glenview, Illinois
Boston, Massachusetts
Chandler, Arizona
Upper Saddle River, New Jersey

ISBN-13: 978-0-328-53764-8
ISBN-10:   0-328-53764-0

1 2 3 4 5 6 7 8 9 10 V011 19 18 17 16 15 14 13 12 11 10
CC1

ISBN-13: 978-0-328-53764-8
ISBN-10:   0-328-53764-0

PART 1: COMPREHENSION

Directions

Kayla wants to make the world a better place. Read the selection to see how she might solve her problem. Then answer Numbers 1 through 11.

Kayla's Problem

"It's just so frustrating to be in that under-fourteen category," muttered Kayla. "You want to do your bit to make the world a better place, but nobody lets you if you're not already fourteen."

"Well," said Kayla's mother, giving her daughter a meaningful glance, "you could always try cleaning up your room."

"Right, Mom, that's just what I had in mind as my contribution to the good of humanity."

"On a serious note, Kayla, I really appreciate all you do around here—taking care of your brothers after school and getting dinner ready for all of us."

"But I want to do something that helps other people—people outside our family. Whenever I try to volunteer, they tell me to call back when I'm finally fourteen—a whole year-and-a-half from now. And you remember the disaster of my attempts to convert Charlie into a therapy dog."

Hearing his name, Charlie thumped his bushy golden tail, smiled up at Kayla, and resumed his nap. "Kayla, I admire your eagerness to make a difference," her mother reassured her and then resumed entering data into her computer.

Seeing that Charlie and her mother were clearly preoccupied, Kayla retreated upstairs to telephone her friend Claudia. No answer. Out of sheer boredom, Kayla started to neaten up her room. In the process, she found an interesting-looking magazine halfway through a pile of discarded clothes. Flipping through it, she completed a personality inventory, calculated her body-mass index, and coveted a pair of pink suede sandals.

Suddenly she stopped flipping and concentrated on a full-page ad that showed a child with a bald head. "Would you be willing to help this child?" asked the headline in 24-point type. The ad explained that the child was suffering from a medical condition that caused hair loss. It explained that many children were in similar situations and could be helped by volunteers willing to donate their hair for prosthetic wigs. Kayla read through the list of conditions—hair at least ten inches long after braiding, no dyed hair, no gray hair—and realized that she met all of them. The sponsoring organization was actually seeking donations from young people.

Kayla walked to her mirror, picked up her hairbrush, and pulled it gently through her long, slightly wavy, red hair. She loved her hair and the way that everyone commented on it. The question was, how much did she love it?

Then she remembered the picture of the child and thought about her own good fortune. Her hair would be short, but not gone. And it would grow back. Kayla made up her mind. The ad had said that parental permission was required, so Kayla picked up the magazine and headed downstairs.

"Hey, Mom," she said. "Can I interrupt you for just a minute to talk about something important?"

1 **Based on her actions in the story, Kayla seemed to be**

A athletic.

B idealistic.

C selfish.

D intelligent.

2 **What is the setting of this story?**

F a family home

G a beauty salon

H a business

J a school

3   **From the tone of their conversation, how did Kayla's mother feel toward her daughter?**

A   bothered that Kayla was so messy

B   grateful that Kayla was a good person

C   proud that Kayla did so well in school

D   pleased that Kayla was such a good cook

4   **What was Kayla's conflict in the story?**

F   She wished her mother would pay more attention to her.

G   She was tired of taking care of her brothers every day.

H   She wanted to help people but couldn't find a way to do it.

J   She wanted to use the computer, but her mother was using it.

5   **Which of these events in the story happened first?**

A   Kayla went downstairs.

B   Kayla looked in the mirror.

C   Kayla called Claudia.

D   Kayla opened a magazine.

6   **Kayla probably looked at herself in the mirror because she was**

F   getting ready to go out.

G   considering dying her hair.

H   concerned about her looks.

J   imagining having short hair.

7   **Which of the following things would Kayla be most likely to do?**

A   begin training to run in a competition

B   help her mother clean the house

C   help build a house for a homeless family

D   try out for the middle school gymnastics team

8   **Why did Kayla pick up the magazine?**

F   She wanted to find a way to help others.

G   She was feeling bored.

H   She was trying to decide whether to subscribe.

J   She had to return it to Claudia soon.

9 **What did Kayla probably do next?**

   A   get her mother's permission to go out

   B   start getting dinner ready for the family

   C   ask her mother for a ride to Claudia's house

   D   talk with her mother about donating her hair

10 **The conversation at the beginning of the story foreshadowed which later event?**

   F   Kayla's mother working at the computer

   G   Kayla's dog working as a therapy dog

   H   Kayla's calling her friend Claudia

   J   Kayla's intended plans for her hair

11 **What did Kayla do just after she called Claudia?**

   A   began cleaning up her room

   B   thought about cutting her hair

   C   looked through a magazine

   D   talked to her mother

GO ON

The Man Behind the Prize

Every year a few people from different places in the world are awakened by
a telephone call at dawn. The caller tells them they have been chosen to receive
the world's most prestigious award: a Nobel Prize. These prizes are granted every
year in the fields of literature, physics, chemistry, medicine, economics, and peace.
Nobel Prizes convey instant fame on those who win them. Much less famous is the
man behind the awards. His name was Alfred Nobel.

Nobel was best known in his own time as the inventor of dynamite. He held over
three hundred patents on his inventions and was one of the richest people in the world
when he died in 1896. In his will, Nobel left much of his money to establish prizes
for those who "have made the greatest contribution to serve mankind."

Nobel was born in 1833 in Stockholm, Sweden. His father, Immanuel Nobel,
was an engineer and inventor who built bridges and buildings. In 1837, Immanuel
traveled to Russia to find work, and his wife remained behind and supported
the family by opening a grocery store. In Russia, Immanuel became rich and

successful. His greatest accomplishment was to convince the Russian tsar, or leader, to build floating defenses to protect St. Petersburg from British attack. In 1842, the Nobel family was reunited in St. Petersburg. The four brothers, including Alfred, received the best education available in the world. His father hired private tutors to teach the boys languages, literature, and science. When they were older, they traveled abroad to study with the world's most famous scientists.

Alfred Nobel wanted to become a poet, and later on he wrote poetry and plays in addition to his scientific work. However, his father wanted him to become a chemical engineer. Therefore, in 1850 he sent Alfred to a private laboratory in Paris. There Alfred met Ascanio Sobrero, an Italian chemist who had recently invented nitroglycerine. Nitroglycerine is a highly explosive liquid—much more explosive than gunpowder. In fact, it was considered too dangerous to be of any practical use. Nobel wanted to develop a safer form that could be used in construction projects. He pursued this interest in Russia and later in Sweden.

Working with nitroglycerine was dangerous. Nobel's experiments killed several people, including his younger brother, Emil. When the city of Stockholm outlawed the experiments, Nobel continued them on a barge on a nearby lake. Finally, after many years of work, Nobel figured out how to make nitroglycerine into a paste that could be formed into rods. In 1867, he patented his invention, which he called dynamite. Together with several new types of drills that were invented around the same time, dynamite was responsible for a worldwide increase in building. Using the new technology, engineers built bridges, tunnels, roads, and railroad lines. Nobel formed companies that profited from the technology.

Eventually, Nobel built factories in several countries. He built laboratories in his homes in Sweden, Scotland, Italy, France, and Germany. He traveled frequently and became involved in political movements as well as business and science.

Nobel was strongly influenced by Bertha von Sutter, the leader of an international peace movement. She worked for Nobel briefly as his secretary and remained his friend for decades. After Nobel's death in 1895, it was discovered that he had left much of his immense fortune to establish the Nobel Prizes. Bertha von Sutter herself won the Nobel Peace Prize in 1905. Other famous winners have been Martin Luther King Jr. and Presidents Jimmy Carter and Barack Obama.

Why would the inventor of dynamite establish a peace prize? Nobel himself always thought of his invention as benefiting humanity. Beyond that, his motives will perhaps remain a mystery.

12 **Which statement based on the selection is the author's opinion?**

F The Nobel Prizes are the world's most prestigious awards.

G Nobel Prizes are granted every year.

H Nobel Prizes are given in the fields of literature, physics, chemistry, medicine, economics, and peace.

J Winners of a Nobel Prize receive a telephone call at dawn.

13 What was the author's purpose in writing this selection?

A to present the positive and negative results of an unusual invention

B to express personal opinions about the Nobel Prizes

C to inform readers about a man who had a lasting impact on the world

D to persuade readers of the importance of the Nobel Prizes

14 Which event happened last?

F Immanuel Nobel moved to St. Petersburg.

G The Nobel sons studied languages and literature.

H Alfred Nobel studied in Paris.

J Immanuel Nobel helped defend St. Petersburg.

15 Which of the following generalizations about inventions is supported by this selection?

A Most inventions result from team effort.

B Most inventions come about by accident.

C Most inventions require years of work.

D Most inventors become very wealthy.

16 Where did Nobel first become interested in nitroglycerine?

F Paris

G Scotland

H Stockholm

J St. Petersburg

17 Why did Nobel want to invent a safe form of nitroglycerine?

A so that it could be used instead of gunpowder

B so that it could be used in construction

C to help protect the St. Petersburg harbor

D to make his factories less dangerous for his workers

18 What is the most likely reason that Nobel established prizes for science, literature, and peace?

F to include all his many interests

G to reward people who worked for him

H to reward people who prevented wars

J to honor the memories of his father and brother

19 What is the fifth paragraph mainly about?

A the use of dynamite in construction

B the development of an invention

C the dangers of nitroglycerine

D Nobel's use of dynamite to make profits

20 According to the selection, what is an important difference between nitroglycerine and dynamite?

F Nitroglycerine is more expensive to use.

G Dynamite can be used for warfare.

H Nitroglycerine is safer than dynamite.

J Dynamite can be used for construction.

21 Based on the information in the selection, what conclusion can you draw about Alfred Nobel?

A He was primarily interested in making money from his inventions.

B He concentrated on how to help his country defend itself in war.

C He was active in promoting the cause of peace during his life.

D He was interested in the peaceful uses of his inventions.

22 What is this selection mostly about?

F the establishment of the Nobel Prizes

G the life and times of Alfred Nobel

H the invention of dynamite

J the recent winners of the Nobel Peace Prize

GO ON

Directions

Write your answer to Question A on the lines below. Base your answer on the two selections you have read.

A What did Kayla and Nobel have in common? Provide evidence from each selection to support your answer.

WRITING ACROSS TEXTS

_____

_____

_____

_____

_____

_____

_____

_____

_____

Directions
Read about poor people in different places around the world and one idea for how to help them. Then do Numbers 23 through 33.

A Different Kind of Bank
The World's Richest and Poorest Countries

The United Nations uses the Human Development Index (HDI) to compare human well-being around the world. The HDI is based on life expectancy and education, as well as on income. Based on the HDI, Table 1 shows the world's 15 richest and 15 poorest countries in 2008.

HDI Ranking	Country	Location	Life expectancy at birth (years)	Gross domestic product* (GDP) per person ($)
1	Iceland	Europe	82	35,814
2	Norway	Europe	80	51,862
3	Canada	North America	80	36,687
4	Australia	South Pacific	81	33,035
5	Ireland	Europe	79	40,823
6	Netherlands	Europe	81	36,099
7	Sweden	Europe	81	34,056
8	Japan	Asia	82	31,951
9	Luxembourg	Europe	79	77,089
10	Switzerland	Europe	81	37,396
11	France	Europe	80	31,980
12	Finland	Europe	79	32,903
13	Denmark	Europe	78	35,125
14	Austria	Europe	80	35,523
15	United States	North America	78	43,968
165	Rwanda	Africa	46	819
166	Ivory Coast	Africa	48	1,632
167	Guinea	Africa	55	1,118
168	Mali	Africa	54	1,058
169	Ethiopia	Africa	52	700
170	Chad	Africa	50	1,470
171	Guinea-Bissau	Africa	46	467
172	Burundi	Africa	49	333
173	Burkina Faso	Africa	52	1,084
174	Niger	Africa	56	612
175	Mozambique	Africa	42	739
176	Liberia	Africa	45	335
177	Congo	Africa	46	281
178	Central African Republic	Africa	44	679
179	Sierra Leone	Africa	42	630

* **Gross domestic product** refers to the value of everything produced in a country in a single year.

Awa is a young widow who lives in Burkina Faso, a nation in West Africa. She has six children, and when her husband died she had no way to support them. She started various small businesses selling vegetables, dried fish, and butter. Finally, a microloan of just $100 allowed her to buy cooking pots and other kitchen supplies, and she began to prepare and sell cooked food on the street. This business is profitable enough to allow Awa to support herself and her children, as well as to repay the loan.

An even smaller loan helped Etagegn, an Ethiopian widow, rise out of poverty. She and a group of friends borrowed $60 and used the money to buy materials to build fuel-saving stoves. They began selling the stoves to neighbors in their rural village and soon were earning a good income for their families. They too were able to repay the loan, and the money they paid in interest allowed the bank to make new loans to other very poor people.

Zekaraya, a fourteen-year-old boy, lives in Egypt. He used to sell noodles on the street to help support his family. However, a small loan has allowed his parents to open a noodle shop. With their increased income, his parents can now afford to send their children to school. Zekaraya sometimes works in the shop, but he has time to study—and he is no longer bullied by gangs of boys out on the street.

Awa, Etagegn, and Zekaraya all benefited from microcredit, a special type of finance aimed at the very poor. According to the Grameen Bank of India, which originated the concept, microcredit makes small loans to very poor people. These loans allow people to establish small businesses that generate income. In this way, these people become able to care for themselves and their families. And as they repay the loans and pay interest on the money they have borrowed, more money is available to help other people.

The origins of microcredit can be traced to 1976, when an economics professor in Bangladesh, Muhammad Yunus, started a research project. Professor Yunus thought that if poor people living in rural areas were given access to money—even very small amounts of money—they would be able to start their own businesses and support their families. At the time, Bangladesh was suffering from a severe famine, and Yunus had begun to doubt the effectiveness of the classical economic theories he had been teaching. "I found it difficult to teach elegant theories of economics in the classroom. . . . I felt the emptiness of those theories in the face of crushing hunger and poverty," he explained.

Yunus's research project, which originally operated only in a small part of one province in Bangladesh, had expanded into a neighboring province by 1979. In 1983, it evolved into the Grameen Bank, which was chartered by the government to provide seed money to allow poor people to start their own businesses. Today, the Grameen Bank is 90 percent-owned by its borrowers and 10-percent owned by the government of Bangladesh. It has 2,548 branches and almost eight million borrowers, of whom 97 percent are women. It provides services in every village in Bangladesh. In addition, the bank serves as a model for other banks and organizations in South and Central America, Asia, and Africa, which now lend small amounts of money to poor people.

Yunus's idea, which seems so simple and obvious today, has helped untold millions of people. In 2006, that idea earned him the world's most prestigious prize: the Nobel Peace Prize, awarded jointly to Yunus himself and to the Grameen Bank.

23   Which of the following can readers conclude from the fifth paragraph?

A   There were a small number of people who needed loans.

B   Banks did not make loans to poor people.

C   Economists did not do enough research.

D   There were no banks in Bangladesh.

24   Which of the following statements based on the selection is the author's opinion?

F   Yunus's idea is simple and obvious.

G   Yunus won the Nobel Peace Prize in 2006.

H   Yunus's project started in a small area.

J   Yunus got his idea during a time of famine.

25   How are Awa and Etagegn alike?

A   Both make and sell stoves.

B   Both have opened restaurants.

C   Both go to school.

D   Both are widows.

26   Which of the following statements about microcredit is supported by the selection?

F   Microcredit is just one idea for helping poor people succeed.

G   Microcredit has helped many poor people, as well as their societies.

H   Microcredit is responsible for helping poor women get an education.

J   Microcredit is now focused only on countries in Africa.

27   Why is Zekaraya now able to go to school?

A   He no longer has bullies bothering him on the street.

B   The Grameen Bank built a school in his village.

C   Parents who receive loans must send their children to school.

D   His parents earn enough money in their shop to send him to school.

28   According to the table, where are most of the world's richest countries located?

F   Africa

G   North America

H   Europe

J   Asia

29 What was the author's purpose in writing this selection?

A to inform readers about an unusual way to help poor people

B to persuade readers to take action to help poor people

C to entertain readers with individuals' life stories

D to present historical facts about the Grameen Bank

30 Which event in the selection happened last?

F There was a famine in Bangladesh.

G Yunus won the Nobel Peace Prize.

H Yunus began a research project.

J The Grameen Bank was founded.

31 Why did the author of this selection include the table?

A to show the need for microcredit projects

B to show that Bangladesh is not among the poorest countries

C to show how poor the poorest countries are

D to show countries where Grameen Bank has been active

32 According to the table, in which two countries do people live the longest?

F United States and Austria

G Netherlands and Sweden

H Iceland and Norway

J Iceland and Japan

33 According to the table, which two countries have the lowest gross domestic product per person?

A France and Finland

B Central African Republic and Sierra Leone

C Iceland and Norway

D Burundi and Congo

Copyright © Pearson Education, Inc., or its affiliates. All Rights Reserved.

Directions

Write your answer to Question B on the lines below. Base your answer on "The Man Behind the Prize" and "A Different Kind of Bank."

B The purpose of the authors of both "The Man Behind the Prize" and "A Different Kind of Bank" was to inform. Explain how each author organized information to achieve that purpose.

_____

_____

_____

_____

_____

_____

_____

_____

PART 2: VOCABULARY

Directions
Mark your answer choice for Numbers 34 through 48.

34 Which word has a suffix that is used to create a noun from a verb?

  F meaningful

  G gently

  H contribution

  J disaster

35 The story "Kayla's Problem" used the phrase *prosthetic wigs*. If you wanted to look up the word *prosthetic* in the dictionary, between which pair of guide words should you look?

  A proton—prow

  B professor—promote

  C proper—protein

  D propel—prose

Use these entries from a dictionary to answer Number 36.

> **sheer**[1] (shir), **1** *adj.* complete; absolute: *sheer nonsense, sheer weariness.*
> **2** straight up and down; very steep: *From the top of the wall it was a sheer drop of 100 feet to the water below.* **3** very thin; almost transparent: *Those sheer curtains will let the light through.*
>
> **sheer**[2] (shir), *v.* to turn from a course; turn aside; swerve: *At the last minute, the boat sheered away from the rocks.*

36 Which meaning of *sheer* is used in the following sentence?

  Out of sheer boredom, Kayla started to neaten up her room.

  F sheer[1], definition 1

  G sheer[1], definition 2

  H sheer[1], definition 3

  J sheer[2]

37 What does the word *coveted* mean in the following sentence?

Flipping through the magazine, she completed a personality inventory, calculated her body-mass index, and coveted a pair of pink suede sandals.

A bought

B wanted

C imagined

D put away

38 Read this sentence from "Kayla's Problem."

Kayla found an interesting-looking magazine halfway through a pile of discarded clothes.

The word *discarded* has the prefix *dis-*. What does *discarded* mean?

F not wanted

G too wanted

H wanted again

J possibly wanted

39 Read this sentence from the selection "The Man Behind the Prize."

In 1842, the Nobel family was reunited in St. Petersburg.

The word *reunited* has the prefix *re-*. What does *reunited* mean?

A not united

B too united

C united again

D possibly united

40 What is the base word of *prestigious*?

F prestig

G rest

H prestige

J ous

GO ON

41 The word *will* has several meanings. Which meaning is used in the following sentence?

In his will, Nobel established prizes to be awarded.

A a helping verb that indicates action in the future

B a helping verb that expresses an order

C a power of the mind

D a legal document

42 Which pair of words lists synonyms?

F physics—medicine

G benefiting—helping

H inventor—businessman

J relatives—executors

43 What is a synonym of the word *immense*, as it is used in the following sentence?

After Nobel's death in 1895, it was found that he had left much of his immense fortune to establish the Nobel Prizes.

A ill-gotten

B inherited

C lucky

D huge

44 What does the word *access* mean in the following sentence?

If poor people were given access to small amounts of money, they would be able to start their own businesses and support their families.

F the right to use something

G the right to enter a place

H an admission ticket

J an interest-free loan

Use this entry from a dictionary to do Numbers 45 and 46.

> **ben•e•fit** (ben´ ə fit) **1** *n.* something that helps or promotes well-being: *Free speech is a great benefit to democracy.* **2** *n.* financial help in time of sickness or old age: *Social Security pays monthly benefits to elderly people.* **3** *n.* an entertainment or social event intended to raise money for a charity: *The luncheon is a benefit for the police auxiliary.* **4** *v.* to aid, advance, or improve: *Our cause has greatly benefited from your donation.*

45 According to the dictionary entry, the word *benefit* can be used as which two parts of speech?

A adjective and noun

B noun and verb

C verb and adverb

D adverb and adjective

46 Which dictionary definition of *benefit* is used in the following sentence?

Awa, Etagegn, and Zekaraya all benefited from microcredit, a special type of finance aimed at the very poor.

F definition 1

G definition 2

H definition 3

J definition 4

47 The word *microloan* has the same prefix as the words *microscope* and *microcosm*. What is the meaning of the prefix *micro-*?

A small

B slow

C poor

D good

48 What is the base word of *effectiveness*?

F effective

G factual

H effect

J fictive

PART 3: WRITING CONVENTIONS

Directions
Mark your answer choice for Numbers 49 through 60.

49 Which sentence is an imperative sentence?

  A When did you last see her?

  B Please don't slam the door.

  C His name is Boris.

  D What a fine job he did!

50 Which sentence is a compound sentence?

  F When the game was over, everyone cheered.

  G Maureen and her cousin Sean visited their friends last week.

  H His father is an artist, and his mother is a doctor.

  J David heard the alarm clock ring and got out of bed.

51 Which sentence has an action verb?

  A Josh feels happy this morning.

  B The weather will seem warm tomorrow.

  C Megan sometimes becomes tired at school.

  D The dog looked warily at the cat.

52 Which sentence has an indirect object?

  F The band's music sounds good.

  G She gave her father a card.

  H We swam in the pool yesterday.

  J The girl in the red dress is my friend.

53 Nicole split the apple into two equal _____.

  A halves

  B halfes

  C halvs

  D halfs

54 The judge decided that Alyssa's science project was the _____ one in the science fair.

   F best

   G most good

   H goodest

   J better

55 Neither my brother nor my sister _____ well.

   A sing

   B are singing

   C sings

   D be singing

56 Henry should _____ home earlier than he did.

   F of gone

   G had going

   H have gone

   J have went

57 The dog ran away with the _____ toy.

   A babys

   B baby's

   C babys'

   D babies

58 Which sentence is written correctly?

   F He asked "if dinner was ready?"

   G "Who has my book," Charles asked.

   H Kyle asked what time is it?

   J Amber asked, "Is it over yet?"

GO ON

59 **Which sentence is written correctly?**

   A   Clara speaks spanish very well.

   B   Brandon used to live in canada.

   C   Matt moved out of town last Winter.

   D   Victoria has a Mexican pen pal.

60 **Which sentence is written correctly?**

   F   Leave a message for her and I.

   G   Let's go to their house.

   H   Him and me like to study together.

   J   Ask them to help theirselves.

PART 4: WRITING

PROMPT

Alfred Nobel made a fortune from his invention of dynamite. Muhammad Yunus had an important new idea. Your world is shaped by many new ideas and inventions. Think of an idea or invention you consider important. Write an essay that will convince your reader of the importance of the idea or invention you chose. Give reasons to support your viewpoint.

CHECKLIST FOR WRITERS

_____ Did I think about a new idea or invention that I consider important?

_____ Did I take notes for my paper about the idea or reasons I think the idea or invention is important?

_____ Did I organize my paper in a logical way?

_____ Did I use words and details that clearly express my ideas and that will convince others that the idea or invention I chose is important?

_____ Do my sentences make sense?

_____ Did I check my sentences for proper grammar and punctuation?

_____ Did I check my spelling?

_____ Did I make sure my paper is the way I want readers to read it?